BEHIND THE RIDE

How Disney Imagineers Deliver the Magic

DAVID MUMPOWER

Editor: Bob McLain
Layout: Artisanal Text

ISBN 978-1-68390-219-5
Printed in the United States of America

Theme Park Press | www.ThemeParkPress.com
Address queries to bob@themeparkpress.com

CONTENTS

INTRODUCTION

From a young age, we fell in love with the idea of the ride. No matter which theme park or carnival that we visited, we knew that the mechanical wonders that we boarded were special treats, some of the best parts of childhood. Even something as simple as the rockin' horsey at the grocery store that cost a quarter still provided a certain oomph that made us feel special.

For many of us, that sensation never diminished. We loved rides then, and we still love them today. Whenever a new one opens, we rush to experience it for the first time. Then, we circle back to our favorites and ride them again. Theme park fans are an eclectic bunch. We want the new hotness, but we adore the comforting embrace of the classics.

I'm just like you. I love these thrills and want as many of them as I can get. Some vacationers travel to exotic destinations, foreign countries where they can learn other cultures. Well, I've been to my share of international locales and hope to go back one day. When I plan my next trip, however, I still circle back to the wide world of Disney. I loved it as a kid, and I never outgrew it as an adult.

I'm also someone who wants to know how things tick. I'm not someone who can rebuild a car engine like my brother or maintain a nuclear power plant like my other brother, but I share their interest in the mechanics of moving parts. I want to know what's under the hood.

Just as importantly, I want to position myself in the same spot as Imagineers back in the day when they planned the next great Disney ride. I seek to understand the challenges that they faced. It's the best way to appreciate what these visionaries accomplished when they built the most iconic theme park attractions of all-time.

Walt Disney and his team don't receive all of the credit, though. Humanity's lust for thrill rides existed long before Disneyland opened its gates to the public. In fact, fans of Space Mountain owe a great deal of gratitude to Russian sledders. Their passion for quick, borderline suicidal trips down Russian mountains was an unlikely starting point for the modern roller coaster.

The first chapter of this book will recount the fittingly circuitous path that led to the great coaster wars of modern times. It's an oddly nationalistic argument, too. From there, I'll deconstruct the mechanics of nearly 30 of Disney's most famous attractions. I'll evaluate everything from engineering to manipulation of the senses. The goal is to demonstrate just how meticulously Imagineers plot ride immersion.

Disney wants you to believe in what's happening. They seek to bring back some of that childish wonder that you lost along the way. They know that when they do their job right, they'll deliver a ride experience that makes you feel like a kid again. Let's go behind the ride to learn all of the tricks they've performed over the years to achieve this ambitious, noble goal.

CHAPTER ONE

THE CURIOUS ORIGIN OF THE MODERN ROLLER COASTER

Did you know that you have winter weather to thank for the existence of roller coasters today? Yes, the ski slope is more than just the place you go before you get an air cast. It's also the accidental inception of theme park thrill rides.

Tidbits like this permeate the history of the modern roller coaster. When you think of the architectural marvels in place today, you're likely to focus on the metal alloys and feats of engineering that brought your favorite coaster into existence. A lot had to happen throughout the past two centuries for roller coasters to reach their current form today, though.

Numerous Guinea pigs, some of them unwilling, had to fall and/or slide down some of the steepest inclines on the planet in order for Space Mountain to become viable. They had to break more bones than your average X-Games participant for the sake of knowledge. Yes, innovation requires sacrifice, and the early days of roller coasters were more about trips to the hospital than the advancement of science.

Over time, park curators grew smarter. They learned from the litany of shattered femurs and separated shoulders. In between concussions, victims of early attempts at thrill rides passed down their knowledge to these more cautious observers. The end result is that each iteration of what we now call the roller coaster streamlined and enhanced the process.

Riders outgrew those prototype models that were the equivalent of Slip 'n' Slides on ice. They built a better coaster cart and tracks with less friction to propel adrenaline junkies down the path. The 20th century left behind the odd choices of noted coaster junkie Catherine the Great (no, really) and advanced the premises of the Mauch Chunk Switchback Railway into the first Coney Island roller coaster. All it cost those original theme park tourists was a nickel to ride.

From there, a lot of what you know of roller coasters today became a reality. Early computers empowered visionary engineers to build a better version of the concept, a Scenic Railway that could sweep the passenger away into a fictional realm. A few plucky pioneers led the charge in elevating roller coasters from a cheap thrill into something more stable and satisfying.

No matter how much of a coaster enthusiast you are, the history of this thrill ride may shock you. To fully understand it, we must trace its roots back to the 17th century as an ice ride, debate which country has a rightful claim to the world's first roller coaster, and track the evolution from ice-dependent sled into a gravity-fueled coal mining train cart. Then, we'll look at how a Coney Island update changed everything as wood roller coasters became the industry standard. Finally, we'll examine how Walt Disney and the team at Arrow Development revolutionized the industry by crafting the world's first steel coaster, the Matterhorn Bobsleds, the ride that closed the circle from sledding to...sledding. Buckle up your safety harness! You're in for a thrilling ride through the history of the roller coaster!

RUSSIAN MOUNTAINS AREN'T MOUNTAINS AT ALL

Thrill rides have come a long way since their humble beginnings. The proof of this lies in the origin story of the roller coaster. What Russian citizens in the 17th century called roller coasters are what you call sleigh rides today. The explanation for the Russian Mountains as a thrill is obvious. Russia is home to the North Pole of Cold, the place where the lowest temperature on record occurred. Ice is the country's most abundant resource.

Some enterprising predecessors of today's adrenaline junkie culture learned that they could pass the cold winter's months in a thrilling way. All they had to do was improve the sled ride. How does one do that? They increased velocity.

If you grew up in a region that has snow, you did this as a child as well. All the kids in the area know where the tallest hills are, the ones that are best for sledding. On snow days, they head over to these areas and take turns zooming down the hill.

The same premise applied in the 17th century. Russians had an unfair advantage, though. They had so much cold weather that they could maximize each sled ride. They'd manufacture entire hills of ice, packing the snow underneath for support. The ice would provide the optimal velocity for a sled ride into oblivion.

As is the case with most adrenaline junkies, however, Russian Mountains fans eventually decided that the regular version of sledding wasn't enough. They needed more. These enterprising coaster fanatics enjoyed one of the greatest breakthroughs in the history of our industry. Their epiphany was that they could build a supporting lumber track for their sled path. Yes, almost five centuries ago, a basic version of roller coaster tracks existed. Their sole purpose was to increase the velocity of sleds.

The premise worked similarly to how you board a roller coaster today. Russians would climb up a set of stairs to the top of the tracks, the exit point for a grand adventure down the ice slope. In many instances, two tracks were built together. That allowed the rider to exit one track and immediately have access to the other.

Over time, the tracks of Russian Mountains also evolved. A straight line is fun, but twists and turns are even better. Every coaster enthusiast knows this, but it was something of a revelation in the 1600s and 1700s. Even a 30-degree turn seemed like an amazing improvement at the time.

Designers built new coaster tracks that provided riders with an unprecedented level of enjoyment. The new tracks were as much as five stories high and up to three hundred feet, providing exceptional ride length relative to early versions of Russian Mountains. The 17th century sled rides were so accomplished that you still see a variant of them today. Many ski slopes offer the same type of downward track sled ride. Oddly, water parks do as well, although theirs substitute water pressure for the slippery nature of ice.

The reason why this invention has stood the test of time involves one royal fan. History has recounted many tales of Catherine the Great, one of the most storied female rulers of all time. The luminary who led her country through the Russian Enlightenment, Catherine II had a few eclectic hobbies, and was one of the strongest proponents of Russian Mountains, commissioning some of her most inventive citizens to build a better ride. Catherine the Great's passion for Russian Mountains in combination with her people's passion to please her led to something shockingly close to a modern roller coaster track.

RUSSIA, FRANCE, AND THE UNITED STATES GO TO WAR...OVER WHEELS

The next huge advance in the roller coaster industry is all thanks to the French. At least, that's what they'd have you believe. The same is true of Russia, while the United States has an attraction of its own that can prove their point.

The debate is simple. Which country was the first to add wheels to a sled? Yes, that seems like an innocuous topic, but it's also the holy grail of roller coaster history. The first person to accomplish this simple addition, putting wheels on a sled, is also the one who invented the roller coaster cart—and the roller coaster itself. You can understand why each country is so emphatic that they deserve the credit.

Russia's argument is the most organic one. They maintain that it was a natural step for one of their innovators to take an invention they'd already created and enhance it. After all, most of what I just described in the past section stems from precisely this process. As is the case with those irrefutable claims, this one involves Catherine the Great.

Allegedly, one of her minions, James the Third, delivered an edict to the people of Saint Petersburg. He wanted a new iteration of the Russian Mountains to show his ruler. She was looking for something new and exciting after literally hundreds of sled rides on the original version. This might be historically inaccurate, though. Catherine the Great was 55 at the time, which is like 75 today. She was either right at or just beyond the average life expectancy of the era. Imagine your grandmother on Fury 325, and you can form your own opinions on the plausibility of this scenario.

Assuming the entire story isn't apocryphal, one of the royal subjects developed a roller coaster cart at the Gardens of Oranienbaum in Saint Petersburg, which was the mecca of Russian Mountains tracks. It was a carriage rather than how conventional coasters look today, and it bounced over the hills awkwardly. That's probably why it didn't find immediate success. Allegedly, this event transpired in 1784, which is important since the French claim didn't happen until 1817. The American version, the quantifiable one, also didn't arrive until 1827, so the Russians do have the best claim to the world's first roller coaster.

THE WHEELS OF BELLEVILLE

Why does France disagree? The honest answer is that they probably want to have a claim to such a historic event. Also, they didn't have a thrill-seeking granny begging for energy drinks and a daredevil ride experience as their claim of authenticity. In Russia, grandmothers run over reindeer. I now offer my apologies to Yakov Smirnoff haters, whose numbers should be legion.

Anyway, the more diplomatic explanation is that even if Russia did put wheels on a sled first, what they created wasn't truly a roller coaster in any realistic sense. In 1817, France improved on the premise with a pair of its own inventions.

The first of them, Les Montagnes Russes à Belleville, doesn't receive as much recognition. Even its name hints at its derivation. It basically translates as The Russian Mountains of Belleville, which sounds like a Sylvain Chomet movie rather than a roller coaster innovation. This is presumably why the French focus on The Promenades Aeriennes in Parc Baujon when they make their claim.

The Promenades Aeriennes featured a symmetrical design that looked almost like the infinity sign. That's a sideways 8 if you're not into math. The difference is that rather than a curve in the middle, it had a straight line down the center of the track. Roller coaster enthusiasts are already putting two and two together on this one.

Yes, the two tracks operated independently but simultaneously. Yes, it's a type of ride design still in place today. If you've ever been on a coaster like Gemini at Cedar Point, you know the deal. The French version wasn't quite that polished, as the coaster carts only passed at a single point at the bottom, at which point each one climbed a lift hill. So, there was a bit of a race at the end where the riders could view the adjoining track. That great idea in coaster design you've loved since you were a kid is three centuries old.

Amusingly, the better argument for the French inventing the roller coaster is at Les Montagnes Russes à Belleville. It was there that a true advance in coaster design happened. Some enterprising Frenchman had the marvelous idea to tether the cart to the track. Russian Mountains always had a chance for the sled to come off the ground, which any six-year-old will tell you is a lot of the fun. To maximize velocity, however, keeping the cart attached is much better.

The Belleville ride achieved this by slotting grooves into the tracks. Then, it used the axles of the wheels to roll through these grooves. Through this methodology, the coaster cart could maintain its speed while staying under control and following the path. Ride engineers and enthusiasts today know this same strategy by a different term, underfriction. Some ingenious French citizen developed the premise three centuries ago yet they received no recognition for their profound discovery.

USA! USA!

While all three of roller coaster carts are verifiable and thereby valid claims of a sort, an American still claims the honorary title of Father of the Roller Coaster. His name is LaMarcus Adna Thompson, and he was a wildly successful businessman. In lingerie sales. The history of the roller coaster includes some truly bizarre anecdotes.

Thompson proved at a young age that he owned an inventive mind. When he reached adulthood, he set up shop in Elkhart, Indiana. It was here that he developed an amazing device that could manufacture women's hosiery without damaging the products. Since hosiery tears so easily, early machines struggled to mass produce nylons. Thompson's system vastly enhanced the output of products relative to raw materials used. He earned a fortune selling stockings, but years spent in a small manufacturing facility degraded his health. Thompson found himself forced away from the industry that had made him independently wealthy.

With newfound riches and ample free time, Thompson sought a new hobby. He discovered inspiration during a vacation to Pennsylvania. In the eastern portion of the state, he stumbled on a local tourist attraction that would become his obsession. Before we evaluate his impact on the industry, however, the Pennsylvania ride deserves its own discussion.

WHEN IS A RUNAWAY TRAIN CALLED A ROLLER COASTER?

The answer to this riddle is when it's called the Mauch Chunk Switchback Railway instead. If you're a coaster enthusiast, you've likely heard of this vehicle before. It's unmistakably the ancestor of the modern roller coaster. The difference is that coasters today don't include a side of black lung stemming from a ride alongside a ton of coal.

The explanation for the unusual circumstance of a trip down the Mauch Chunk Switchback Railway involves its stated purpose. At first, it was just a train crisscrossing Pisgah Mountain, one of the Appalachian Mountains in that part of Pennsylvania. During the early 19th century, pioneers discovered a massive coal deposit in this region. The problem they faced was how to mine it effectively. Pisgah Mountain has an elevation of 1,557 feet, which is problematic enough in the 21st century. Two hundred years ago, the idea of harvesting those natural resources bordered on impossible.

The Lehigh Coal & Navigation Company embraced this challenge, and the fruits of their labor sustained the company for more than a century. They laid tracks nine miles downhill from the summit of Pisgah Mountain to the more serviceable area below. Gravity was their friend in this endeavor. If you put any wheeled vehicle on the top of a hill then give it a push, it'll slide down at a steadily increasing pace. If you put a ton of coal on the vehicle, it goes much, much faster. You can see where I'm going with this.

The place at the bottom of the mountain, the ultimate destination of all the mined coal, was then known as Mauch

Chunk. The workers here spent their days watching a runaway train zoom downhill for 14 kilometers before semi-gracefully stopping in town. The path the train traveled was on rails, so it was safe (ish). The day laborers discovered that they could pass the time in much more entertaining fashion if they hopped a ride from the top of the mountain down to Mauch Chunk. It quickly became the thing to do in town. The locals called it the Gravity Train, and the path it followed was the Gravity Road.

The specs of the train were modest, but the seeds of a roller coaster existed. The Gravity Train became so popular with tourists that an entire line of railway closed for mining purposes. It became a permanent attraction that built up quite the reputation on the East Coast. By the 1850s, guests were willing to pay between 10 and 50 cents to ride, depending on the season and popularity of the Mauch Chunk Switchback Railway. Yes, surge pricing has been around more than 160 years.

FATHERING THE MODERN ROLLER COASTER

Imagine Thompson's excitement when he reached Mauch Chunk. His life's work was no longer possible, and he was actively seeking new inspiration. There, in a coal miner's town, he stumbled across a nascent technology brimming with possibilities. A man of science and invention, he quickly deduced that this idea would prove even more popular in a larger metropolitan area. All he needed to do was find a way to craft a man-made mountain in a small space.

The name is misspelled on the patent, but his application begins thusly:

> Be it known that I, LA MARoUs A. THOMP- soN, of South Chicago, county of Cook, and State of Illinois, have invented certain new and useful Improvements in a Roller Coasting Structure, of which the fol-lowing is a full. clear, and exact description, that will enable others to make and use the same, reference being had to the accompanying drawings-forming a part of this specification.
>
> This invention relates to an improved coast ing structure to be used as a means of pleasure and-amusement; and it consists of certain novel featuresin the construction and

> arrangement, as will be hereinafter more fully set forth and claimed. (sic)

He closes the application with the most important details:

> Having thus described my invention, what I claim as new, and desire to secure by Letters Patent, is—
>
> 1. In a coasting structure, the combination, with the tracks B B, running parallel with each other and having the starting and terminal stations at the same elevation, of the switch-tracks E F, whereby the car reaching the terminus on the outgoing track is transing trest1e-w0rk C and the platform (1 and ferred to the return-track and back again to d of the same height, substantially as de the first track for another trip, substantially scribed. as described.
>
> 2. In a coasting structure, the combination, with two parallel tracks or road-beds having undulating grades or planes, of the support LA MARCUS A. THOMPSON. \ Vitnesses...

What you can draw from this information is that A) a top inventor of hosiery machines and roller coasters doesn't bother to master spelling and punctuation and B) Thompson was so confident in the originality of his man-made structure that he patented it to prevent copycats from benefiting from his sweat of brow.

That leads to an important caveat. A gentleman named John G. Taylor also patented something that could be loosely described as roller coaster technology in 1872. The Baltimore resident also earned one patent for his work, but he never received the same credit as Thompson. That's presumably because Thompson wound up with roughly 30 patents related to roller coasters, as he constantly sought to perfect the process. Meanwhile, Taylor only gained a single one, patent 128,674, which was for an "Improvement in inclined railways." Engineers who have studied Taylor's patent vs. those of Thompson rightfully consider what Thompson did critical to the modern roller coaster.

The other key aspect of the conversation is that no confirmed evidence exists that Taylor ever built the coaster for which he received a patent. Some Baltimore newspapers reference it, but the only picture of something that could qualify lacks a confirmation date. It's entirely possible that Taylor built a coaster that precedes the famous one at Coney Island by a decade or more. There's just no evidence of it. That's why Taylor is anecdotal in discussions of roller coaster history while Thompson is revered as the founding father of the industry.

WELCOME TO CONEY ISLAND!

1884 was the most important year for roller coaster innovation prior to the opening of Disneyland. That year, Thompson unveiled the Gravity Pleasure Switchback Railway at Coney Island. It was an immediate blockbuster success. Part of the explanation was location. While Coney Island only claims a population of 25,000 even today, it is readily accessible from all boroughs of New York City. Even during the 1880s, 1.2 million people lived in the city. It was already the most populous one in the United States. Putting the world's first roller coaster nearby was one of the best business moves in the history of amusement parks.

While eastern Pennsylvania coal mining towns don't have a lot of national status, a ride like the Switchback Railway at Coney Island immediately garners international headlines. The 19th century equivalent of theme park tourists flocked to this new sensation, paying a nickel a ride. Thompson once reported that he earned $600 daily during the early years of the Switchback Railway. That's the equivalent of $14,634 today. The marvel here is that at a nickel a ride, we're discussing 12,000 customers per day. And this wasn't a ride that had the massive throughput you'd see at a theme park attraction today. The demand for the Switchback Railway was off the charts.

Thompson had followed up his success in the hosiery industry with what we'd now describe as a five million dollar annual revenue stream—from a single ride. Soon afterward, the inventor began duplicating his coaster track at other locations across the country. Within four years, 50 different Switchback Railways existed. He understood that competitors were quickly copying his lucrative idea. By building his own constructs, he could ward off imitators before they gained a foothold in the coaster industry he effectively created. In addition to being the Father of the Roller Coaster, Thompson also possessed business acumen on a par with Walt Disney. The two men were kindred spirits separated by two generations.

What made the Switchback Railway so innovative? That's the critical part of this discussion. We've learned how ice slopes turned into railways and how sleds turned into roller coaster carts. The parallel from Russian Mountains to the Switchback Railway goes beyond these terms, though. Thompson used the premise as a baseline for his attempt. He built a pair of symmetrical courses next to one another. From a side view, they wouldn't look the same since the start of one was the end of the other and vice versa. They were structurally identical, though.

Where his concept differentiated itself from Russian Mountains was in the addition of hills. You know them today as air-time, but that's a comically extravagant description of what the Switchback Railway offered. We're talking about a very slight raise in elevation before an almost immediate decline. It's like when your car travels over a hill. You go up and then down almost instantly. This bit of non-linear riding qualified as a major breakthrough in the 19th century.

The speed of the Switchback Railway was so mild that you likely jog faster. It went six miles per hour for roughly 600 feet. The start of the ride began 50 feet in the air, requiring another ladder climb to get to the coaster cart. Again, it was similar to the Russian Mountains save for the fact that all motion was man-made rather than ice-based. He constructed a roller coaster cart on wheels that rode the track layout to the bottom then circled around, the switchback part of the railway.

Since the earliest known roller coaster didn't require ice, it could operate all year, differentiating it from Russian Mountains. It also didn't need an additional incline to move like the sled-based iterations of the concept. While it was a gravity ride in both design and name, the Switchback Railway was the first coaster of its kind to deliver a guided trip. The tracks determined the course, and the wheels kept the cart on the path. It was in all ways what we have come to consider a roller coaster, which is why Americans have a good claim as the originators of the modern version.

Since Thompson so carefully mimicked the themes and ideas of Russian Mountains, however, they too have a valid claim. Without their ideas—and the support of Catherine the Great—the Father of the Roller Coaster never would have built the Switchback Railway. Then again, just to mess with your head a bit, the Russian phrase for roller coaster translates as American Mountains, so the terms the countries use seem stubbornly chosen to cause the highest level of confusion.

ANOTHER CONEY ISLAND CLASSIC

The first phase of the roller coaster design war transpired at the turn of the 20th century. By this point, it was an international sensation. Developers tried to one up one another by adding faster speeds and more bumps. Both the French and Americans crafted vertical loops in their tracks, which sounds like fun in theory. These early versions suffered from reckless engineering, the type we'd call carnival quality today. On multiple occasions, riders fell out of the coaster cart during a loop. Ride harnesses were barely more than safety straps at the time, assuming any sort of precautionary gear was in place. What mattered most to coaster constructors was attendance, something that hasn't changed much over time.

Jack and Irving Rosenthal noted that the strongest coaster sales remained in Coney Island, presumably because the tourist area offered the original and catered to a huge metropolitan area. They invested $100,000 in 1925, the equivalent of $1.4 million today, to build a more modern take on the coaster premise. By then, the Switchback Railway was 40 years old... and not their property. They needed a thrill ride of their own.

Their new roller coaster ran way over budget, more than 75 percent by some estimates, but the end result was worth it. The ride known as The Cyclone became one of the all-time staples of amusement parks. When it debuted, this ride cost a quarter, and guests happily spent that amount. They still do. Almost a century later, the price is a factor of 40 larger. That's roughly triple its inflationary rate. Despite the stiff spike in cost, guests at Luna Park happily pay to take their place in history as one of the tens of millions of humans who have ridden The Cyclone.

What makes the ride so special? Realistically, it's the sense of history. Even though it's only 85-feet high, it does stretch 2,640 feet, giving it a ride time of almost two minutes. It offers a 60-degree drop and can reach 60 miles per hour today, quite a bit more than its original version. As the single most popular wooden roller coaster of the first half of the 20th century, The Cyclone stands out for its heritage more than its specs, though.

THE BRIDGE TO MODERNITY TRAVELS THROUGH THE MATTERHORN

The history of the roller coaster comes full circle with the Matterhorn Bobsleds, which opened to the public in 1959. It was the first steel coaster, which is reason enough to mention it. What's more interesting, however, is what the Matterhorn represents. The genesis of the roller coasters we enjoy today was Russian Mountains. And these constructs were little more than glorified sleds placed on controllable paths.

What's the Matterhorn? It's a steel roller coaster that simulates the experience of sledding down the side of a mountain. In other words, it's a metallic Imagineering re-creation of Russian Mountains. Your mind should be blown right about now.

Whether Walt Disney appreciated the symmetry of his creation is up for debate. Uncle Walt loved the incongruity of theme park tourists enjoying a snow day at a southern California theme park. The weather would never allow that, so ride designers had to bring the snow each day. They also needed an attraction that could outdo standard roller coasters of the day.

Since a roller coaster arms race had been ongoing for decades when Disneyland opened, their version had to blow the competition out of the water. Otherwise, critics would lambaste Imagineers for delivering something ordinary. This was the driving impetus in many of their technological innovations of the 1950s and 1960s. The press forced Imagineers to compete against their own reputation and legacy more than against other ride developers.

The idea of the Matterhorn came with a conceptual crisis. Unlike conventional sled rides, bobsleds twist and turn a great deal. When a person jumps on a sled, they head straight down unless something goes horribly awry (and I have the stitches to prove it). The bobsleds made famous at the Winter Olympics twist through hairpin turns that a basic sled couldn't match. Disney's vision for the Matterhorn exceeded any possible implementation of Russian Mountains.

Such innovation brought technical challenges. Regular wood tracks don't bend the way that Disney needed. Also, they didn't provide the freedom of movement a bobsled required. The ride cart needs to slosh around the turns. Otherwise, the rider will understand that they're on a rail system, ruining the illusion of the experience, a huge no-no at Disney, even during the 1950s.

Uncle Walt had already conceded on one of his early demands. He'd wanted actual snow at the Matterhorn, a functional impossibility. He wasn't about to capitulate on a quality bobsled simulation, too. Disney checked in with his friends at Arrow Development, similarly inventive ride designers that had built six of the opening day rides at Disneyland. He trusted them to provide an honest opinion about the feasibility of his idea while hopefully providing quality input on how to construct it.

The finest minds in theme park ride development put their heads together and came up with something revolutionary. They recognized that steel could bend in ways that exceeded wood. Thanks to some deft metallurgy, the two companies crafted the world's first tubular steel track. It could twist and turn at angles that were functionally impossible with wood. The continuous track allowed multiple coaster carts to ride on the track at once, and the tubular nature of the tracks meant that the carts could zoom past one another at key points, a feature that remains a highlight of the Matterhorn to this day.

The introduction of steel in coaster development meant everything to the modernization of track design. The massive heights and extreme velocities of giga- and strata-coasters are only viable now thanks to steel alloys that conduct heat quicker and more reliably. More importantly to Disney, the bobsled simulation was extremely authentic since the curved track felt just like an actual bobsled course. Riders could easily imagine themselves participating at the Winter Olympics as they streaked down the steel track. It's one of the greatest attractions in the history of Disney. More importantly, it's the roller coaster innovation that led directly to extreme velocity, maximum G's, constant airtime thrill rides that adrenaline junkies adore today.

The most amazing part of the evolution of the modern roller coaster is how circular it is. Russians started with sleds that they sped down icy slopes. Then, they added tracks to maximize velocity. Over the centuries that followed, other inventors took those same ideas and meshed them with other innovations such as the train. They also threw in some gravity for good measure to deliver a better rush for their guests.

Afterward, a savvy American lingerie manufacturer developed a cart with wheels and a man-made track that didn't need ice to operate. His version of the wood roller coaster became the standard that dominated the industry for several decades until a different ride in the same Coney Island area took that title.

Some 30 years later, Walt Disney and his Imagineers decided that they wanted to construct their own roller coaster, but they didn't want it to seem like anything already in existence. They chose a new material for their tracks, and steel became the new standard in the industry. But how Disney used it is the most beautiful part. They chose to build...a mountain sled ride. If Catherine the Great were alive today, the Matterhorn at Disneyland would remind her of home. That's because it's the Russian Mountains attraction that Russians never made.

CHAPTER TWO

MR. TOAD'S WILD RIDE

Did you know that the Happiest Place on Earth contains a portal to Hell? No, this isn't metaphorical and no, I'm not joking. A cheeky attraction at Disneyland has the darkest ending imaginable for a dark ride. People get run over by a train and sent to Hell. How is that even possible? Let's go behind the ride to discover the tricks that Mr. Toad's Wild Ride plays on unsuspecting guests.

THE EXPERIENCE

Bringing the story of "The Wind in the Willows" to life

THE TRICK

Choosing to have form follow function

Fittingly, Ichabod Crane is partially responsible for the journey to Hell. Had his tale of woe taken longer, Walt Disney would have created an entire movie from the premise. Instead, Uncle Walt chopped the tale of the Headless Horseman into half of an animated film called *The Adventures of Ichabod and Mr. Toad*. The second half retold the story of *The Wind in the Willows*, the children's novel by Kenneth Grahame. And a simple modification of that tale became the basis for Mr. Toad's Wild Ride.

When Disney constructed the Happiest Place on Earth, he chose Fantasyland as the themed area that would replicate his movies. It's why Fantasyland at Disneyland has so many attractions. They're largely based on Disney animated tales, and it was especially true for the rides available on opening day.

As Imagineers culled the list of potential attractions, they realized that the arrogant J. Thaddeus Toad, Esq. and his passion for motor vehicles naturally led to the perfect ride construct. They could re-create the wild ride that led to Mr.

Toad's incarceration in the books, but the way they chose to implement it was surprising.

The ultimate form was a modification of an earlier concept. Did you know that Mr. Toad's Wild Road was intended as the first roller coaster at Disneyland? Yes, years before the Matterhorn debuted, Disney executives had already debated a coaster, one that would have been there on opening day!

Arrow Enterprises, the construction group that built the hardware, was an expert in coaster design. Disney spoke with them about a roller coaster that would bounce haphazardly through the park and offer guests the fear that they were about to wreck into vehicles at Disneyland's parking lot. For obvious reasons, Uncle Walt felt this idea wasn't family-friendly enough, but he still loved the elegantly simple concept that drove the pitch: a wild ride. How would Disney bring the idea to life?

Three of the original Disneyland attractions show rather than tell events from famous Disney films. Those attractions are Peter Pan's Flight, Snow White's Scary Adventures, and Mr. Toad's Wild Ride. In each example, Imagineers attempted to place the audience in the shoes of the protagonist. For Peter Pan and Snow White's presentations, many guests left the ride feeling a bit confused. Mr. Toad's Wild Ride, on the other hand, received instant acclaim due to the cleverness of the design.

Guests boarded a vehicle, and then they hurtled along a seemingly random path of unlikely places, each of which presented more danger than the last. The form of the ride naturally followed its function. It was a chaotic trip through London that caused harm to Toady, his friends, and virtually everyone else in his path. In short, the title of the attraction aligns more tightly with its underlying premise than anyone had ever seen before or ever would again at Disneyland.

THE EXPERIENCE

Bringing the city of London to life

THE TRICK

Detailed artwork and breathtakingly colorful illustrations

Part of the reason for the ride's triumph is its attention to detail. From the start, the theming at Mr. Toad's Wild Ride sets it apart from other early attractions. Imagineers transferred all of their illustration skills from years spent making animated movies to the design of the ride. They crafted meticulously detailed sets that brought the vision of Grahame's novel into the real world.

From the moment that guests boarded their vehicles, they got swept into this artificial reality due to its believable design. The little touches sprinkled throughout the attraction pulled guests into this colorful mansion and forced them to believe that they were on an ill-fated journey through the London countryside.

The journey begins in Toad Hall, the mansion owned by Mr. Toad. Perfect details like a brick fireplace and elegant chandeliers bring the world of The Wind in the Willows to life. Murals hang from the walls, the décor is immaculate, and you'll totally believe that you're in the stately manor of an established professional. Then, the jalopy starts...

The trick of Mr. Toad's Wild Ride is also its conceit. On most dark rides, the vehicle controls the pace in a way that you have plenty of time to take in the sights. The ride cart is a timed mechanism that takes you from set piece to set piece, ensuring that you see what you're supposed to see at the perfect moment. Mr. Toad's Wild Ride is like that, only it works with a significant degree of difficulty.

Your ride is wild, which means it whizzes through several sets at breakneck speed. If you don't pay attention, you might miss a key element. This explains why Imagineers pulled out some unusual tricks for the sets. The colors are brighter and more vibrant because they have to be. To follow the story as intended, these visuals must grab your attention quickly. They only have a brief instant to do so before you're careening down the path to the next thing.

Whether you're rumbling through the library of Mr. Toad or bouncing through the countryside (and terrifying innocent sheep), everything on the ride happens FAST. There's a distinct "blink and you'll miss it" vibe to this attraction that is rare today and was absolutely unprecedented in 1955. The ride takes less than two minutes, and it feels even faster due to the adrenaline rush of breaking through brick walls, triggering explosives, and crashing into trains.

The imagery of Mr. Toad's Wild Ride is everything on this ride. Without those colorful displays, the imperiled MacBadger's tenuous ladder would mean nothing. You wouldn't care that Moley's chicken dinner is ruined. Those pesky weasels wouldn't seem like unwelcome home invaders. Why, you wouldn't even notice that you've finished a lightning-fast descent into Hell. The vivid, dazzling artwork is what brings the wild ride to life. Of course, it has a little help...

THE EXPERIENCE

Making the ride wild

THE TRICK

Engaging in a bit of motormania

The kinetic nature of the wild ride dictates that your vehicle keeps you on a fast pace. You're not supposed to have time to catch your breath. Mr. Toad is driving poorly, and you're stuck in the jalopy with him!

The car is integral to the ride experience. Imagineers went out of their way to craft a memorable buggy that looks the part. It's a stubborn throwback to classic cars of yore, ones that didn't have roofs. When you're on this ride, there's nothing between you and the ground, amplifying the stakes as you rumble out of control through the London sights.

Motor Mania is the cheeky term used for Mr. Toad's Wild Ride, and the car seems right out of Chitty Chitty Bang Bang. It's a classic buggy with a steering wheel that does absolutely nothing. The bright color of the vehicle blends well with the overall scheme of the attraction, where every visual stimulates the eyes.

The cute factor of the Motor Mania lineup is that each vehicle has its own name. Many of the characters from *The Wind in the Willows* appear during the ride. Alert fans will notice that the rest of the gang still has a token presence in the names of the vehicles.. You'll know which car you're in by the moniker printed on the front. Options include Toady, Badger, Ratty, Mole, MacBadger, Cyril, Winky, and Weasel.

Originally, there were 12 Toad cars in the fleet. Nine would operate at once, while the other three would stand by, waiting to take new riders off on a thrilling journey into eternal damnation. The first vehicles were remarkable achievements in theme park design, too.

Arrow Enterprises used roughly 200 pounds of fiberglass and sheet metal to build the fleet. These parts were among the first ones to arrive during Disneyland construction, which means that Mr. Toad's Wild Ride is in the conversation for the first true theme park attraction. And the Toad cars were very well constructed at that. These vehicles lasted almost 40 years before Disneyland finally had to replace them. To the very end, they still reinforced the mayhem that is Mr. Toad's journey into Purgatory.

THE EXPERIENCE

Hell on Earth

THE TRICK

Creating the ultimate hot spot at Disneyland

There's a tongue-in-cheek element to Mr. Toad's Wild Ride. The attraction draws inspiration from the novel and the movie adaptation, but the final scene on the ride is its own creation. Imagineers chortled at the thought of a proper comeuppance for Mr. Toad, an individual whose obsession with reckless driving led to his imprisonment.

In the book and the film, he managed to escape. At Disneyland, he's...less fortunate. The wrong turn at the wrong moment causes the wild ride to end in tears. Mr. Toad suffers a head-on collision with a train. He doesn't survive. Yes, this odd quirk of storytelling sends the rider straight to Hell! How very Disney, right?

While no one can know for sure why Walt and his team of Imagineers went so dark on this particular dark ride, Mr. Toad's Hell is an unforgettable scene. The key is that Disney plays the scene for comedic effect. The judge who just sentenced you to prison is in Hell, too. In his new role as ultimate arbiter of souls, the judge is basically the same, save for his horns and more sinister pointing.

To create the effects of Hell, Imagineers didn't have to work very hard. It's one of the simplest tricks on any Disney attraction. They simply had to turn up the heat to make the place feel like a furnace...well, an eternal furnace. Other than that, the tricks are still the same: colorful paintings and a hellscape of a set.

Well, okay, there is *one* trick that's a bit different. A fire-breathing green dragon ominously torments you with flame. Of course, it's just backlit. Fire doesn't shoot out or anything. The green dragon is the final ghoul before you escape from here and return to the Happiest Place on Earth, ending your wild ride safely.

Well, you're safe from a physical perspective. You might be emotionally scarred by the cardboard cutouts that just attacked you and then damned you for eternity. Seriously, this ride isn't what you'd expect from Disney. I'm not sure that an Ichabod Crane/Headless Horseman attraction would have been darker in tone.

CHAPTER THREE

PETER PAN'S FLIGHT

When Walt Disney World opened in 1971, 23 attractions were part of the new theme park. Only three of them were new; the rest were duplications of existing attractions at Disneyland. Due to construction issues, three more rides appeared later in 1971. When we fast forward to today, only a handful of the rides, shows, and events available in 1971 still exist.

Out of those legendary attractions that embody the origins of the world's most popular theme park, only one still comes with a consistent hour-long wait. Whether you believe that omnipresent line is due to its sustained demand or some issues with ride throughput, the attraction is undeniably popular to this day. So, let's go Behind the Ride to learn more about Peter Pan's Flight, from its original version up to the recent modifications.

THE EXPERIENCE

Creating the illusion of flight

THE TRICK

Building a better boat

In the days preceding the Omnimover, Disney Imagineers invented numerous ways to load passengers on ride carts. The initial plans for Peter Pan's Flight, however, required a tremendous amount of innovation. The attraction would lift people up in the air and make them soar through the London skyline on their way through Neverland. That's an entirely different type of movement than for attractions like Autopia, or Mr. Toad's Wild Ride. The riding apparatus would have to pull guests into the air safely, similar to a Ferris wheel, and then it would have to guide them on a fixed route through various set pieces.

Suffice to say that there was no technology available that could perform such aerial maneuvers. Marvin Davis, a recent hire of WED Enterprises, received the request to build a functional lift apparatus early in his tenure at the company. He had to create a ride system that would hook to a track on the ceiling. In order to create the appropriate sensation, Davis and his cohorts designed a new kind of ride cart.

This contraption is called an Aerial Galleon, and you know it as the flying boat that operates similarly to a ski lift carrying you up into the sky. It perfectly mimics the sensation of flying over London. More impressively, the ride track manages this while delivering one of the smoothest ride experiences at Walt Disney World. Most of Disney's attractions are intentionally rough at times. The ski lift mechanic somehow seems tranquil as it elevates. Disney planners intended guests to feel like lifting into the sky via magic is a fluid and calm process rather than a bumpy ride.

One noted improvement occurred at Walt Disney World over Disneyland. In order to handle the larger crowds in Orlando, Florida, Disney built a better boarding/de-boarding area. They discarded the regular loading and unloading methodology at Disneyland in favor of Omnimovers. So, as long as the lines are at Walt Disney World today, the situation could have been much worse without that bit of forward thinking.

THE EXPERIENCE

Making guests feel like Peter Pan

THE TRICK

Learning from the mistakes at Disneyland

While Peter Pan's Flight wasn't ready at the start of Walt Disney World, it *had* debuted on opening day at Disneyland. Given the long list of catastrophes that occurred there on the nightmarish first day at Uncle Walt's first theme park, the problems with Peter Pan's Flight certainly didn't stand out. Still, an ongoing issue existed. People really didn't get the ride.

You have to remember that in 1955, Walt Disney tried to differentiate the Happiest Place on Earth from the similar entities of the era. Those were circuses, carnivals, and haunted houses. None of those places offered anything resembling Peter Pan's Flight. Ostensibly, that was a competitive advantage for Disney. In execution, it led to a lot of confused customers. Theme park rides are a lot like jokes. Something's gone wrong if you have to explain what should be self-evident. With jokes, that's the punchlines. With theme park rides, it's the experience that everyone should innately understand.

The concept of Peter Pan's Flight is right there in the title. The idea is to elevate the rider into the sky so that they enjoy the sensation of flying through the clouds, just as Peter Pan can. The problem with selling products to consumers is that they have a tendency to be literal. While other characters in the story of kids swept off to Neverland are memorable—especially dastardly Captain Hook, mercurial Tinkerbell, and strong heroine Wendy—none of them are as important as the titular lead. The fact that Peter Pan's Flight didn't feature Peter Pan annoyed guests.

In the early days of Walt Disney World, Imagineers had to address the concern over the absence of Peter Pan. Their iteration of the flight included a stronger link to the character, which was part of the attraction at Walt Disney World. All they had to do was focus on the one aspect that got lost in creating the Disneyland version of the attraction. Peter Pan's Flight had to include Peter Pan in the story. It seems so simple in hindsight, yet the amazing cast members of the Walt Disney Company didn't get this right for 16 years. Similarly, they didn't add a Peter Pan audio-animatronic at Walt Disney World until 1983, 12 years after the attraction's Florida introduction and almost 30 years after its Disneyland debut.

THE EXPERIENCE

Creating London and Neverland

THE TRICK

Disney artistry at its finest

Imagineers also had other options to improve the experience while enhancing the connection to the story. Due to the extra land available at Walt Disney World, Peter Pan's Flight spreads out across a larger space. That provides Disney with the ability to include extra set pieces. The larger scale in combination with the employment of audio-animatronic figures brings the realm of Neverland to life in a better way than the attraction's original Disneyland counterpart. To perfect the ride experience, however, they had to re-imagine the journey.

The vessel you board sweeps you into the room of Wendy, John, and Michael Darling. The idea behind the bedroom is that you as Peter Pan are carrying the Darling children off on a grand adventure. Your destination? Neverland!

Imagineers clearly loved the endeavor of bringing Neverland to life. Starting in 1955 at Disneyland, cast members have delivered several iterations of the same concept. The one at Walt Disney World is superior due to the aforementioned space. In 1971, Disney realized that they could add additional elements to an already-popular attraction.

At Walt Disney World, the London skyline extends longer and includes greater detail. Gorgeous fluorescent colors sparkle in the darkest of dark rides, causing London landmarks like Big Ben to glimmer as they glow. The real showstopper of the Florida version, however, occurs at Captain Hook's boat. This vessel is 48-feet-long, large enough to host a duel between Hook and Pan as well as audio-animatronics of all the major characters. And it's soooo shiny. This part of the Peter Pan's Flight journey features virtually every color palette imaginable, and the view is so overwhelmingly bright that it almost scorches your eyes. The final touch that differentiates the Magic Kingdom version is a celebration of the victorious Peter Pan with his beloved Darling children. The attraction encapsulates the joyous exuberance of Peter Pan the Disney movie in barely two minutes of ride-time.

THE EXPERIENCE

An interactive line queue

THE TRICK

Major technological advances

In 2015, Peter Pan's Flight added something that fundamentally changed the aggravation of the ride queue experience. Prior to then, people found themselves standing in the world's most boring line for one of Walt Disney's World slowest attractions with regards to guest turnover. In the wake of the MyMagic+ FastPass changes, would-be Peter Pan's Flight riders generally experienced a wait-time of at least 45 minutes and occasionally as long as 90 minutes.

Imagineers wanted to shake things up, so they added an interactive line queue. Now, guests walk through the bedroom of the Darling children. The queue is now part of the Peter Pan's Flight experience.

3D images of Peter Pan characters set against fluorescent backdrops populate the exterior of the Darling bedroom while embracing the theme of the actual ride. Once you reach the room itself, magic exists in every nook and corner. Tinkerbell spreads her fairy dust on the children's trunk, a globe, and a wall calendar among other things. When you reach a certain wall, you can interact with her simply by waving your hands.

Peter Pan's Flight as originally envisioned thrusts riders into a world where magic exists and Peter Pan fights off adulthood and a one-armed pirate simultaneously. In 1955 and then again in 1971, Disney employees re-created the world as best they could. In 2015, they expanded the range of Peter Pan's powers by introducing a line queue that is quite possibly the most impressive thing Disney Imagineers have created in the 2000s. It's that special. Best of all, it reinforces the underlying theme of the J.M. Barrie story: childhood never truly fades away, sometimes you simply need to sprinkle a bit of pixie dust!

CHAPTER FOUR

MATTERHORN BOBSLEDS

During the late 1950s, Walt Disney and his legendary staff at WED Enterprises shared a grand vision. They intended to bring the majesty of the snowy Swiss Alps to constantly sunny California. The architecture they invented became the basis of the amusement park industry as we know it today. Theirs was truly the first tubular steel continuous track roller coaster, and it was instantly iconic the moment it was introduced to the public in 1959. Whether you've been onboard this historic roller coaster or not, you still know of it. In the days before Space Mountain, it stood as the pinnacle of Disneyland. Let's go behind the ride to learn five amazing facts about the Matterhorn Bobsleds.

THE EXPERIENCE

Bringing an iconic Swiss landmark to California

THE TRICK

Walt Disney's vision

Third Man on the Mountain was a 1959 Walt Disney Productions release starring Michael Rennie, who is only famous for portraying the alien in The Day the Earth Stood Still. Despite the forgettable nature of the mountain movie, it had a profound, lasting impact on pop culture.

During the filming of this production, Walt Disney visited Switzerland many times, falling in love with the beauty of the landscape as well as the sophisticated culture of its people. One day, Uncle Walt felt particularly appreciative of the Matterhorn, the iconic highlight of the Swiss Alps mountain range. Whether true or not, folklore indicates that Disney grabbed a souvenir postcard from a nearby shop and mailed it to one of his employees, Imagineer Vic Greene. The message was simple. "Vic. Build This. Walt." While it reads like a text from a demanding eight-year-old, the simple statement directly led to the introduction of the steel roller coaster.

The long-forgotten part of this story is that *Third Man on the Mountain* was intended to be a blockbuster. Despite a difficult shoot once chronicled during an episode of *Walt Disney Presents*, Disney had a passion for the story. He felt that American teens came across poorly in 1950s cinema, so he wanted to make a movie that showed them in a different light. In order to assure the success of what was the 1950s equivalent of Vertical Limit in terms of breathtaking mountain climbing, Disney tethered the film's promotion to the debut of the Matterhorn Bobsleds. For the grand opening of the attraction, he even had actual mountain climbers scale the man-made structure as if it were a real mountain.

THE EXPERIENCE

Bringing a snowy mountain in California

THE TRICK

Imagineer creativity

Before all the above could happen, there had to be a mountain. Understanding his superior's attention to detail, Greene and the rest of the WED Enterprises team started calculating ways to bring an idyllic mountain setting to Walt Disney World. As they discussed solutions, a giant pink elephant danced in the living room. Disney requested a snowy re-creation of a toboggan ride through one of the highest points in the park. In the 1950s, it snowed about as often at Disneyland as, well, it does today, which is to say virtually never. Even attempting to do so artificially, something the company has mastered over the past 50 years, would've been too tricky in the late 1950s. The Imagineers began to call the unbuilt mountain Snow Hill.

Eventually, they persuaded their boss that a valid re-creation of the Matterhorn was possible. He simply had to relent on the snow part. Rather than creating real snow every day, the Imagineers pointed out that they could simply paint frosty weather on the side of the faux mountain. After all, they were building it from scratch, so they could design it any way they liked.

While the Matterhorn isn't even the tallest structure at Disneyland and hasn't been for several decades now, the initial build was historic. Disney's staff re-created the West Coast version of the Matterhorn to the best of their ability. Even its height, 147 feet, has a precise purpose. It's a 1/100th scale model of the 14,700-foot tall mountain. In 1959, it was the tallest man-made facility in the greater Los Angeles area before corporate skyscrapers became popular during the 1960s.

In order to complete the desired reflection of Switzerland, its builders intentionally designed the mountain to have several gaps. Whenever prompted, Walt Disney gleefully explained the thought process. There were holes in the Matterhorn "because it is a Swiss mountain." That's the difference between amusement parks in 1959 and today. You don't see a lot of cheese puns in modern architecture. Then again, this entire paragraph might confuse you since the Matterhorn doesn't have the holes any longer. Over time, Disney employees accepted that safety concerns deserve prioritization over a sight gag/food pun.

THE EXPERIENCE

Creating the sensation of a sled ride down a giant hill

THE TRICK

Outsourcing

Walt Disney's request for a toboggan ride didn't fall on deaf ears. His employees understood that what their boss really wanted was simple. He wanted guests at the Happiest Place on Earth to enjoy a simulated re-creation of a snow day on a mountainside. Everyone loves grabbing a sled and heading to the top of the tallest hill in town, after all.

Since Disney wouldn't be able to supply the ice, they had to come up with a similar sensation. Their idea was to simulate a popular sport from the Winter Olympics: bobsledding. The issue they faced was that bobsledding came with certain perils that wouldn't be acceptable for casual riders. Disney needed to build something that provided the desired bobsledding sensation while keeping guests safely on rails.

To accomplish their goals, Disney returned to one of their favorite collaborators; Arrow Development. Technically a machine shop in nearby Mountain View, California, the founders of this company quickly developed a close relationship with Disney. He called on them to work on a carousel for Disneyland prior to its debut. Impressed by their work, Uncle Walt continued to outsource assignments to them on seminal projects such as Mr. Toad's Wild Ride, Autopia, and Snow White's Scary Adventure. Once Disney appreciated the challenges of his vision for the Matterhorn's accompanying attraction, he asked them for suggestions on how to make his dream a reality.

THE EXPERIENCE

Building the world's first steel roller coaster

THE TRICK

Steel tracks and a watery brake system

Once Disney was ready to build a mountain, the engineers had to lay tracks to crisscross it. Arrow Development had watched with interest as other companies built steel railing for carnival attractions. They correctly deduced that if they lined up the tracks correctly, they could relay the sensation of sliding down a mountain. More important, the rails would control the path of each rider, thereby guaranteeing their safety.

The tubular track was legitimately decades ahead of its time. It's one of the most stunning breakthroughs in the history of Disney theme parks. By positioning the track through natural slopes and bends throughout the artificial mountain, Arrow and Disney learned that they could control the maximum velocity of riders. They even had the epiphany that two tracks standing side by side, the ones we now know as the Fantasyland and Tomorrowland tracks, could "race." This led to even cleverer track placement wherein the two paths intersected at multiple points. It's become one of the iconic aspects of the Matterhorn Bobsleds.

Perhaps the most inventive aspect of the Matterhorn Bobsleds occurs at the end. In the late 1950s, ride engineers didn't have a strong idea of how to handle braking on steel roller coasters since, you know, there weren't any. Arrow and Disney worked together to come up with a ride sequence that would not only provide a thrill to guests but also utility as well.

The famous splash guests receive as they approach the end of their bobsled adventure isn't just for show. One of the little known secrets about the Matterhorn Bobsleds is how little automation there is in the ride. That's because such technology didn't exist in 1958. The engineers had to build it to have the ride ready by the release of the movie the following year.

Their idea was to build a lift system for the first hill followed by a pair of parallel tubular rails that keep each cart on the designated path. Since the carts only hit these rails at three points during the ride, slowing down the bobsled is a question of physics. The people involved with Matterhorn Bobsleds deduced that adding a splash of water would be a natural way of lowering the cart's velocity. It negates most of the speed riders enjoy during the downhill mountain sledding phase of the ride. It's a brilliant way to solve a problem without impinging on the enjoyment of the guest. In fact, the Matterhorn Bobsleds splashdown greatly enhances the overall experience.

THE EXPERIENCE

The mountain's permanent resident scolds unwelcome visitors

THE TRICK

Harold

By the 1970s, audiences were used to much more exciting enhancements at their favorite amusement parks. Disneyland in particular had invented the field of audio-animatronics as a way of making many of their attractions feel more lifelike. To inject some life into the aging Matterhorn Bobsleds, they chose to add a splash of personality to the ride. By this point, Disney had filled most of the holes in the mountain, making the ride seem more generic. It wasn't even the tallest point in Disneyland any longer, much less the greater Los Angeles area.

Matterhorn Bobsleds was falling victim to father time. In order to restore its glory, Imagineers chose to add some local color. To reinforce the mountain theme, they added...a Yeti. Disney fanatics know him as Harold, and he proved so popular over time that Expedition Everest pays tribute with a much larger, scarier Yeti. While imitation is the sincerest form of flattery, most Disneyland fans favor Harold, the original. He exists in three places on the mountain. One is early in the ride when everyone notices him. The other two are track dependent. Each is only viewable on one side of the track, meaning that riders only see Harold twice per bobsled ride.

The primary purpose of Harold the Yeti is to "scare" people as their bobsleds slalom through his mountainous home. In practice, he's a hilarious enhancement to an already fun ride. The Matterhorn Bobsleds already stood out as a great as well as a historic attraction. The later inclusion of a killer Yeti only made it better.

CHAPTER FIVE

IT'S A SMALL WORLD

Time Magazine claimed in 2014 that they had determined the most popular song of all time. No, it's not "Happy Birthday" and no, it's not a song by Elvis or the Beatles. In their own words, Time Magazine "did the math," calculating that one song was approaching 50 million play-throughs after almost 50 years of its existence (in 2014). The song in question is "It's a Small World" by Richard and Robert Sherman, and it's integral to arguably the most iconic ride at any Disney theme park.

Walt Disney once pitched this attraction as the "happiest cruise that ever sailed." More than half a century after he conceptualized this celebration of international cultures and inclusiveness, it's become the symbolic heart of Disney theme parks, entertaining generations of children (and their parents) with its fervid optimism. Let's take this opportunity to go Behind the Ride to learn five tricks of the trade that have made It's a Small World so iconic.

THE EXPERIENCE

Bringing all the cultures of the world to Disneyland

THE TRICK

More puppets than you'd find on the set of Sesame Street

When we go Behind the Ride on most attractions, the story lies in the engineering details. With It's a Small World, the list of Disney icons who had a hand in its construction is the more noteworthy aspect. As we'll discuss, a pair of Hollywood celebrities, Joan Crawford and Walt Disney, started the project. Then, many of Disney's most famous Imagineers like Rolly Crump, Yale Gracey, Marc and Alice Davis, and Bob Gurr had a hand in its design. In fact, a pair of them, Roger E. Broggie and Bert Brundage, earned a patent for the Omnimover in the wake of designing It's a Small World.

The true hero(ine) of the story is another person near and dear to the hearts of Disney fanatics. Mary Blair's relationship with the Walt Disney Company went back to 1940, meaning that she was more than 20 years into her animation career prior to building the puppets that would become the ultimate legacy of her storied life. Given that she handled colors and styling for Disney classics such as *Alice in Wonderland*, *Cinderella*, and *Peter Pan* and also handled illustrations for Little Golden Books during the 1950s, that's an amazing statement.

During the 1950s, Blair had left Disney to freelance, and one of the reasons why was that she wanted to spend time raising her children. When Uncle Walt called in 1963, he offered her a chance to create puppets mimicking the look and style of children across the world. She couldn't resist the siren song of a return to Disney for this project, and all theme park tourists are grateful. Much of her work is still on display today.

Disney needed Blair because one of the secrets of It's a Small World is that all the dolls are the same. To cut down on the manufacturing time, the company built hundreds of dolls with the same shape and appearance. Blair did the heavily lifting in distinguishing them. She added color to areas such as eye and hair color and skin tone. What was remarkable about her work is that the world was on the precipice of another global conflict at the time. Blair eschewed fear in favor of hope and optimism, crafting happy dolls for all the lands.

The husband and wife team of Marc and Alice Davis handled the rest of the set design. Marc crafted the "movie sets" for each scene, building laudable representations of the various countries. Then, Alice handled the costumes to complete the designs of Blair. The work of these three artists has stood the test of time. Disney is reverential to the original designs for the puppets of It's a Small World. While they're not above adding new ones, they restore rather than replace any of the damaged older pieces.

THE EXPERIENCE

Transitioning a pavilion to its permanent home

THE TRICK

Pixie dust from Uncle Walt himself

The backstory of It's a Small World is every bit as amazing as its popularity and longevity. During the early 1960s, lots of corporations and other enterprises including state governments engaged in an arms race. The ultimate goal was to build the most impressive pavilion at the 1964 World's Fair, a massive event at the time. Many of these industrialists tried to broker deals with Walt Disney and his famous Imagineers at WED Enterprises.

A shrewd businessman, Disney understood that he held all the power in negotiations. So, he persuaded a trio of organizations including Ford Motors, General Electric, and the state of Illinois to agree to his terms. In exchange, he built unforgettable and lasting attractions like The Carousel of Progress, Great Moments with Mr. Lincoln (the genesis of the Hall of Presidents), and a third one that was a last minute addition.

Pepsi Cola had little luck in getting their World's Fair pavilion off the ground. Desperate, they listened to one of their board members, actress Joan Crawford. She recommended that they do whatever was needed to persuade Disney and his team to construct their pavilion. They agreed.

It's a Small World was an immediate hit, and after the following year's World's Fair ended in 1965, Pepsi Cola owed Disney and his team a great deal of money. Cleverly, the entrepreneur agreed to lower the cost of payment on one condition: they had to pay to transport the entire attraction to Disneyland, where it would take up permanent residence.

Uncle Walt capitalized on the pop culture awareness of the 1964 World's Fair, marketing one of his pavilions on Pepsi Cola's dime. Then, he again got them to foot the bill in relocating it to his storied theme park, where it quickly became one of the most popular attractions. It's a Small World was already in operation at Disneyland by May of 1966, barely seven months after the World's Fair ended. Some of the items transported from New York famously still have the 1965 shipping stickers on them.

Disney earns a lot of positive press these days for their acquisitions of Pixar, Marvel, and Star Wars on the cheap. What the company founder accomplished with It's a Small World rivals all of these business deals.

THE EXPERIENCE

A trip around the world in 15 minutes

THE TRICK

Building the "little boat ride" that Uncle Walt had envisioned

Today, everyone's familiar with the Omnimover as a concept. A series of connected ride carts move at a set speed along a conveyor belt. It's a ride cart system that offers benefits to the person in the vehicle as well as those operating it. Via the omnimover, a theme park attraction will position the rider precisely where they need to be to enjoy the spectacle. While you're enjoying the ride, the park employees know exactly where you are and how long you'll take.

Disney and their successors employ Omnimovers as a way to control throughput *and* rider safety. Your ride cart is on rails the whole time, both pushing along to the next waypoint and guaranteeing that you don't stray off the course into more dangerous areas strewn with mechanical moving parts. Simply stated, the Omnimover is *the* most important innovation in theme park history. And its roots trace back to the development of what Walt Disney described as a "little boat ride." You'll soon discover that It's a Small World isn't an Omnimover attraction, though!

When one of New York's most famous urban planners, Robert Moses, implored Walt Disney to construct a "children's village," the leader of WED Enterprises ran with the idea. He expanded the request, building a world village instead. Each section would reflect a specific culture, and the only way such an offering was feasible was by controlling the speed of movement of pavilion visitors. Disney designed an entirely new ride system for the boats that would float down the man-made waterways of It's a Small World.

You may not realize this, but the original version of the Omnimover came with wheels. Legendary Imagineer Rolly

Crump illustrated mock-ups of the boats. He later recounted, "We would put Walt on a boat that was on wheels and that was elevated to the right sightline, and then push him through the ride." Disney wanted to tell a story similar to a motion picture, which was their default thought process. The Omnimover allowed them to do this; however, It's a Small World didn't have one at the time. Instead, it was the forerunner of the technology.

Disney built the equivalent of aqueducts for It's a Small World. Since they enclosed the space and thereby confined the boats to a linear path, the voyagers on the "little boat ride" were on a one-way ride downstream. Imagineers loved this idea so much that they explored it further, eventually finalizing the premise of joined vehicle carts with the now defunct Adventures Thru Inner Space, which debuted in 1967. That's the takeaway about It's a Small World. Since the boats aren't connected together to keep the chains moving, so to speak, it's not an Omnimover.

THE EXPERIENCE

The world's most impacting earworm

THE TRICK

Inventing a song so positive that it's literally unforgettable

Believe it or not, the music of It's a Small World could have been worse. While a famous online poll once chose the titular song as the most annoying earworm ever, Disney originally had different plans. As the "little boat ride" would pass through each country, the puppets were expected to play the applicable national anthem. One of the Shermans described the end result as "one horrible cacophony," and their friend, Walt Disney, pressed them to craft a piece of music that would save the day.

Given the time constraints, what the Shermans achieved with It's a Small World is among the greatest accomplishments in theme park history. Pressed for time and with only vague details about the attraction that they knew only as an international boat ride, they locked on a single concept. With all the global infighting during the Cold War, the folks politicking missed something obvious. We all share the same sun and moon, no matter the matter where we hold citizenship.

The lyrics quickly flowed from there.

Still, the Shermans faced an uphill battle during the creative process. Uncle Walt had warned them that any lyrics that they wrote had the following stipulations: "It had to be simple and translatable, and yet it had to be repeated so often over a 14-minute ride that it couldn't be boring." Instructions like that are how we wind up with "Who Let the Dogs Out." Somehow, the talented duo tapped into the same vein of optimism as Blair had. Ultimately, a song that they figured would be forgotten the instant the 1964 World's Fair ended has now been played more than any other piece of music ever. And they should get bonus credit for predicting the social media era half a century out with the lyric, "There's so much that we share."

Disney was so appreciative of the contributions of Mary Blair that she earned a spot on the ride. She's flying from a balloon in the Eiffel Tower scene in Paris. Look for a blonde woman wearing glasses. Otherwise, she might blend in with the other 300+ dolls that comprise the attraction.

One of the explanations for the ubiquity of the song is that Disney never copyrighted it. As a celebration of inclusion, Uncle Walt and the Sherman Brothers chose not to do so, making it a gift to the world.

Pepsi was the original sponsor for the ride, but it was supposed to have a different name. They were trying to honor a popular charity with their attraction. The awkward title for the World's Fair was Pepsi-Cola Presents Walt Disney's "It's a Small World"—A Salute to UNICEF and all the World's Children. Call it The Phantom Menace for short.

Twenty-nine different countries are represented on the attraction, and the song is performed in five languages. As long as you speak English, Italian, Japanese, Spanish or Swedish, you can understand it. Whether that's a net positive is in the eye of the beholder.

CHAPTER SIX

PIRATES OF THE CARIBBEAN

Perhaps no ride is as indelibly linked to Walt Disney as Pirates of the Caribbean, which is bittersweet since he didn't quite live to see its park opening. He died only a few months prior to the debut of what would become a defining Disney attraction. Thankfully, the Imagineers that Uncle Walt had trained were dutiful in honoring his memory. They worked diligently to craft a masterpiece worthy of the everlasting reputation of their beloved boss. And the ride they built has stood the test of time.

Disney unearthed other ways to expand the reach of the concept. The *Pirates of the Caribbean* franchise has earned $3.73 billion in worldwide box office and counting. It's the popular film adaptation of the even more popular Disneyland attraction. People love both so much that they sometimes forget that the ride pre-dates the movie by almost 40 years.

Pirates of the Caribbean's roots go back so far that future film star Johnny Depp was only four years old when Disneyland introduced the ride to the public, while Keira Knightley and Orlando Bloom wouldn't be born until 10 and 18 years later. It's that old, which makes its sustained excellence all the more impressive. You've almost certainly jumped in a boat and headed through pirate country at some point. Let's take this opportunity to go Behind the Ride, explaining all the brilliant, eternal aspects of one of the greatest theme park attractions of all-time.

THE EXPERIENCE

The iconic pirate set pieces

THE TRICK

A boat ride instead of a museum

When you board your hardy vessel and cross the narrow sea to Disney's re-creation of the Louisiana Bayou, you're effectively entering a Disney movie set. Uncle Walt loved to frame his attractions in this way, and he realized toward the end of his life that Pirates of the Caribbean might be his swan song. Disney suddenly learned that he was in the final days of cancer as his Imagineers worked on the ride. Its quality was so important to him that he asked for one last contraption from his Imagineers. They built a gurney system so that he could easily move from set to set at Pirates of the Caribbean. He micromanaged more than usual on the ride, but he didn't live to see the result. The attraction opened at Disneyland three months and 11 days after his death.

The work that Walt Disney surveyed existed across several sets. To orchestrate seamless guest movement from one location to the next, he had to throw out the initial plans for the ride. As originally discussed, Pirates of the Caribbean was intended as a museum celebrating pirate life, especially as told by Robert Louis Stevenson. The author's seminal work, Treasure Island, was a source of inspiration for the attraction.

In order to tell stories akin to those of Long John Silver and Jim Hawkins, Imagineers settled on a few iconic images from pirate lore. They chose many unforgettable visuals such as a cannonball attack from a buccaneering vessel against a well-defended island fortress, a series of imprisoned brigands trying to retrieve a key from an unaware (or too-aware) dog, a pooped pirate clutching a pirate map, and an auction involving justifiably unhappy wenches.

THE EXPERIENCE

Wandering through pirate territory without walking the plank

THE TRICK

A boat ride that started in New York City

The trick the park planners faced was in getting theme park tourists to the proper locations at the correct times. Early stages of their plan didn't require this kind of precision. With a museum design, guests could travel from location to location on their own terms. Once Pirates of the Caribbean changed to a ride, they needed a new strategy. Fortunately, some Imagineers were inventing the technology that would dramatically increase the throughput of the ride. In the preparation phase of the 1964 New York World's Fair, Disney employees faced this issue for multiple pavilions. They eventually realized that a track-based system could provide the rails that guaranteed riders stayed on the correct path AND moved at an acceptable speed.

Pirates of the Caribbean isn't a true omnimover in that the boats don't all connect to one another, but the underlying premise is similar. If anything, it's closest in nature to It's a Small World, and I mean the original version from the World's Fair. Sure, you ride a seaworthy pirate boat that sails from scene to scene, but Disney has your boat on tracks throughout the ride. This innovation is one we take for granted today. It was historic in the 1960s, though. The fake open-ended nature of the ship allows the guest to feel like they're on open sea with navigational charts that can lead to anywhere, but the actual path is finite. Your destination on the watery bayou is fixed. That's also why Disney asks that you keep your hands inside the boat at all times. You could easily catch a finger in the machinery beneath the boat.

The boat ride's quality is due to Disney's diligence. While on the gurney, Disney would go from location to location, demanding to see the set pieces from the same perspective of a future guest. Everything from the original version of the ride that remains is exactly as Uncle Walt intended you to watch it. You're a guest on his movie set when you board Pirates of the Caribbean, and the boat track assures you of experiencing it the precise way that he wanted.

THE EXPERIENCE

Meeting dastardly pirates but living to tell the tale

THE TRICK

One of the first implementations of audio-animatronics (AAs)

Another invention from the 1964 New York World's Fair was the audio-animatronic (AA). The robotic version of Abraham Lincoln was capable of so many movements that critics expressed amazement at its realism. That was the first generation of the software. After the fair ended, Imagineers improved the nascent technology. They understood that Pirates of the Caribbean was a perfect attraction for this style of storytelling.

The purpose of AAs is to mimic human behavior repeatedly during the course of a day. A single AA will have a handful of actions that they perform. Giving one too many mannerisms would require guests to ride multiple times to see the full suite of an AA's programming. With their new attraction, Imagineers wanted a bunch of pirates who would look and act the part without overwhelming audiences. Disney didn't want to scare its guests too much. As silly as that statement sounds, it was a legitimate concern in the early days of the attraction. That's part of the reason why 53 AA birds and animals (such as an adorable key-holding dog) join approximately 70 humans, many of whom are pirates. These creatures provide a soothing backdrop to reassure guests that they'e safe.

What Disney has always loved about AAs is that they're like actors that the company doesn't have to pay. Sure, there's the installation cost and related maintenance fees, but AAs are basically robotic slaves. Each one at Pirates of the Caribbean tells the same story several times every hour. They've done this so well that a few of them have taken on a life of their own. Everyone knows the Pooped Pirate, the husband dunked in water, and the prisoners trying to escape a fire. The technology for these AAs is more than half a century old. The reason why they've maintained popularity is that Imagineers built them so lifelike in the first place. Of course, the most famous AA at Pirates of the Caribbean today is much newer...

THE EXPERIENCE

Watching Jack Sparrow bask in the golden glow of treasure

THE TRICK

Updating a storied ride to reflect a popular movie franchise

Perhaps no attraction at a Disney theme park better exemplifies the timeless but sometimes circular nature of Disney storytelling. At the start of the new millennium, Walt Disney Pictures attempted to evolve several popular attractions into films. Their goal was to enhance the rides by adding a movie presence.

Two of the attempts didn't go so well. *The Haunted Mansion*, an Eddie Murphy movie, exited theaters with only $76 million in domestic box office against a $90 million budget. And you probably don't even remember the other film. *The Country Bears*, based on Country Bear Jamboree, grossed only $18 million, barely half of its $35 million budget. The middle film's popularity makes up for those two disappointments, though. *The Pirates of the Caribbean* franchise became a huge hit, with *The Curse of the Black Pearl* becoming the third most popular movie of 2003. Then, *Dead Man's Chest* shattered the opening weekend box office record on its way to becoming the number one movie of 2006.

To celebrate the hallmark box office achievements, Disney decided to introduce characters from the film franchise into the ride. In other words, the movie based on the ride became the inspiration for parts of the ride that were now based on the movie. I get a headache just thinking about it. Anyway, Disney added Captain Barbossa to the deck of the *Wicked Wench* and Davy Jones and Blackbeard in the opening mists of the attraction.

More importantly, they added a new scene where everyone's favorite miscreant, Captain Jack Sparrow, lives the dream of every pirate. He discovers a room full of gold and jewels that Disney fans suspect is the proverbial Treasure Vault that the Pooped Pirate mentions. The entire set piece is the end of the ride, meaning that a character who didn't exist when Imagineers first created Pirates of the Caribbean is now the showstopper that sends theme park tourists off with a huge smile on their faces. Sparrow is arguably the most iconic new Disney character of the 21st century, and the new version of the ride befits that status.

THE EXPERIENCE

Enjoying a spirited sea shanty

THE TRICK

Teaching an old dog that he was capable of a new trick

When Disney adds atmosphere for a ride, they understand that music sets the tone better than almost anything. That's why so many of your favorite Disney stories include memorable musical accompaniments. They believe in manipulating all five senses as much as possible, and a singalong song is one of their most proven methods to achieve this goal. Even by Disney standards, the backstory for the most memorable song from Pirates of the Caribbean is weird, though.

Xavier Atencio wasn't a music man by trade. He was an illustrator and writer who had started with the company when he was still in his teens. Something Walt Disney loved to do with his employees was challenge them. He felt that forcing someone outside their comfort zone helped them expand their horizons. He would move employees around like pieces on a chessboard, and that's how a writer without a musical background wound up as the lyricist for one of the best loved Disney songs.

At Uncle Walt's request (really, a demand) the man known as X moved to the Pirates of the Caribbean ride. There, he discovered that the project was mostly finished. His boss wanted someone to tie the seemingly disparate pirate stories together, and he believed that X was the man for the job. In a moment of inspiration, the fledgling lyricist determined that a sea shanty was the missing ingredient for this otherwise impeccable attraction. He quickly wrote "Yo Ho (A Pirate's Life for Me)," relying heavily on Disney musician George Bruns for the tune. The song was an instant Disney classic that virtually everyone in the free world can hum, even if they don't fully appreciate what they're doing. The lyrics and music are that catchy.

In an odd bit of trivia, *Pirates of the Caribbean: The Curse of the Black Pearl* wasn't the first instance when a Disney movie used "Yo Ho (A Pirate's Life for Me)." That honor belonged to *Treasure Planet*, a different Disney film honoring the writings of Robert Louis Stevenson. So, two Disney features used the same song in an eight-month period in 2002/2003 after none had in the prior 35 years.

Pirates of the Caribbean is the crème de la crème of theme park tourism. It has name value that far exceeds regular attractions, even ones with sturdier reputations inside the industry. That's because it was the first of its kind, a boat ride through several fictional pirate scenes, all of which earned Walt Disney's personal seal of approval. More than any other attraction, this ride is his legacy, and its impeccable design quality speaks to the work ethic and vision of the man who built the Happiest Place on Earth.

CHAPTER SEVEN

HAUNTED MANSION

Welcome, foolish mortals. Welcome to this special chapter of *Behind the Ride*. I am your special host, your ghost host. You've wondered why hinges creak in door-less chambers, and strange and frightening sounds echo through the halls of the Haunted Mansion. I, your humble narrator from the great beyond, will explain why candle lights flicker where the air is deathly still.

Now is the time when ghosts are present, practicing their terror with ghoulish delight! Kindly step all the way in, please, and make room for everyone. There's no turning back now! Prepare to learn four of the ghastliest tricks at the Haunted Mansion...but remember! There's always room for one more.

THE EXPERIENCE

Me, your enchanting Ghost Host

THE TRICK

Adding a disembodied voice as narrator for each room

In the early days before Disneyland's New Orleans Square even existed, clever Imagineers knew that they wanted a spooky presence at the Happiest Place on Earth. Foolish mortals were in danger of having too good a time. From what I remember of it, life needs balance.

Once Disney finalized plans for my eternal resting place, the Haunted Mansion, they decided that they needed star power, someone to spice up the proceedings of a trip through a gothic manor. They went back to a familiar face or, well, voice. Paul Frees handled many voiceovers for Disney television programs during the 1950s and 1960s. His memorable vocal stylings proved perfect for the caustic, macabre dialogue recited by yours truly.

First, someone had to write my eternally quotable lines, though. A series of Disney employees, including Marc Davis, Claude Coates, Rolly Crump, and Yale Gracey, all contributed ideas to the backstory of the various characters, myself included. Ultimately, the final responsibility fell to X Atencio, who melded together several scary and silly stories about the 999 Ghost inhabitants of the Haunted Mansion.

As the narrator, I have the assignment of letting you know all the important details about the various inhabitants. The dialogue Atencio wrote and Frees recorded for me has remained the same at Disneyland since the introduction of the attraction in 1969. Other non-American parks use different voices for the narrator, but I prefer the classics. Don't you?

THE EXPERIENCE

A ride through the supernatural on a Doombuggy

THE TRICK

One of the first and most recognizable Omnimovers

The debut of the Haunted Mansion was supposed to occur soon after the introduction of Disneyland in 1955, back when I was still among the living. The original maps indicated that this attraction would stand as a major part of the first major park expansion. Fourteen years passed before its actual arrival. Two issues caused the delay. The first was a rift about the tone of the ride, whether it would be funny or scary. The second was whether it would be a ride at all. Some Imagineers argued that it would work better as a walkthrough tour or possibly a museum. You know how stubborn mortals can be.

Walt Disney shelved the debut of the Haunted Mansion due to the indecision, postponing my big moment for more than a decade. He asked his employees to prioritize other attractions that were closer to ready. This delay proved fortuitous thanks to Disney's participation at the 1964 New York World's Fair. During the build-up to this event, Imagineers developed new technology that empowered them to control ride throughput in historically unprecedented fashion.

While constructing four pavilions for the event, Walt Disney and his team discovered the precursor to the

Omnimover. While nothing at the World's Fair technically qualified as a true Omnimover, Imagineers returned from the exhibition with renewed confidence and excitement about future projects. They quickly built Adventure Thru Inner Space in 1967, the first attraction in the world to employ Omnimover technology. Two years later, the Haunted Mansion became the second one, although its vehicular transportation has a bit more je ne sais quoi.

Foolish mortals, I realize that you don't all have Imagineering degrees. Here's what you need to know about Omnimovers. They're called endless transit systems, and for good reason. A chain of vehicles populates a huge track that's hidden beneath the floor. They rotate along a base, creating the illusion of a vehicle moving down a path. The truth is that the chain pulls you around, something that sounds more appropriate for my companions, the Hitchhiking Ghosts.

The Omnimover is how your trip through the Haunted Mansion matches my narration. You're always guaranteed to be in the right space at the perfect moment to enjoy my sardonic wit. The main difference in the Doombuggy from a regular Omnimover is a bit of showmanship, although that's everything in my line of work. Imagineers themed the Doombuggies to make them seem like a moving hearse. They also gave the vehicles the ability to spin, which has become a standard feature ever since. You mortals enjoy this the most as you're twisting through the attic and circling through the graveyard.

THE EXPERIENCE

A room with no windows and no doors

THE TRICK

The world's quietest full-room elevator

Behold my favorite line of dialogue, one I often recite to uninvited guests of the Haunted Mansion:

> Our tour begins here in this gallery where you see paintings of some of our guests as they appeared in their corruptible, mortal state. Your cadaverous pallor betrays an aura of foreboding, almost as though you sense a disquieting metamorphosis. Is this haunted room *actually*

> stretching? Or is it your imagination, hmm? And consider this dismaying observation: This chamber has no windows and no doors, which offers you this chilling challenge: To find a way out!

There is, of course, a way out, and I don't mean my way. The mansion features one of the cleverest designs in the history of Disneyland. Since space was tight in Anaheim, Walt identified a brilliant way to increase the size of his rides. He constructed portions of them in the basement. Imagineers faced a problem, though. How could they lower the guests without their knowing? As always, their solution was stunningly creative.

Do you know how every horror film says, "Don't go down to the basement?" My Haunted Mansion doesn't give you a choice. The octagonal room that you enter when you visit my abode harbors a dark secret. In *Doctor Who* terms (yes, even ghosts watch *Doctor Who*), it's bigger on the inside. The Stretching Room doesn't really stretch. The name is intentionally deceitful. Instead, the room itself moves, operating as an elevator that lowers you to the basement.

The reason you may feel confused is the set of paintings on the walls. They're not extending in size. They're always that length. The trick is that the room obscures your view of the paintings until you begin your descent. As you sink lower on the elevator, you can see more of each image.

Should you ever take a trip up the elevator, you'll notice that the entire picture frame moves, and the size of the display determines how much of the ghastly visages you can view. Our friends in Orlando don't have an elevator. Since Magic Kingdom has plenty of space, the Stretching Room doesn't include a descent. Instead, the ceiling rises. Once again, the original version is superior.

THE EXPERIENCE

A headless groom

THE TRICK

50 years of technological innovations

Constance Hatchaway is a hard woman to love. Despite this statement, many men, possibly even including me, did so. Each one of them was wealthy enough to persuade her to marry, and each of them wound up quite dead because of it.

Specifically, her grooms are dead because of her hatchet, which she swung at each groom with great force. The worst part of the Haunted Mansion is that if your evil bride does kill you, death isn't an escape from her company. Instead, both of you join the rest of the 999 ghosts who live here.

Out of the five men who married Constance, the most noteworthy is...someone else altogether. To add to the perception of Hatchaway the decapitator black widow, Disney added another man to the attic where she resides, a doomed fellow whose head disappeared from his body then reappeared in an unexpected place.

His name was Harry, and a lot of the special effects imagery in the days prior to the opening of the Haunted Mansion mentioned him. That's because the Imagineers loved the concept of a ghost whose head came and went. They used a special effect to disappear the head. Once my home opened to the general public in 1969, Disney employees quickly realized that the disappearing head, well, stayed appearing. The special effect failed under the actual conditions of the functioning attraction. The ambient light near the Doombuggy track undid the trick, and that's why Harry vanished for years.

Ghosts don't stay gone forever, though. My friend triumphantly returned in 2015. More than 45 years later, a new generation of Imagineers found a great solution. They project Harry's face onto a blank head. All that's required to make the top half of Harry vanish into the hatbox is for Disney to remove this face. The space of the blank head now shows nothing. Meanwhile, they project his head in the hatbox. As far as Imagineering special effects go, this one's nothing special, yet it solves a problem that had befuddled cast members for almost half a century!

Now then, we've discussed four carefully kept secrets of my otherworldly residence. Like I said, there's always room for one more, though...

THE EXPERIENCE

Madame Leota hosts a séance

THE TRICK

Putting a head in a floating crystal jar and allowing it to speak

> Serpents and spiders, tail of a rat; call in the spirits, wherever they're at. Rap on a table; it's time to respond. Send us a message from somewhere beyond. Goblins and ghoulies from last Halloween: awaken the spirits with your tambourine. Creepies and crawlies, toads in a pond; let there be music, from regions beyond! Wizards and witches, wherever you dwell, give us a hint, by ringing a bell!

I know this spell all too well. The sorceress named Leota casts it ad nauseam, disrupting the rest of me and 998 of my dearest friends. Technically, an undead spirit herself, Leota is the clairvoyant who allows guests of the Haunted Mansion to participate in her notorious "swinging wake."

The jarring aspect of an encounter with Madame Leota is her appearance. She's a head in a jar a la Futurama. To achieve this effect, Disney recorded images of a person's face that they project into the crystal ball. They didn't hire an actress, though. Instead, it's the work of Imagineer Leota "Toombs" Thomas, which explains the name...although Madame Toombs has a certain ring to it.

Thomas also had the first crack at the voice of Leota. Her coworkers didn't find her menacing enough, though. Disney veteran Eleanor Audley, who provided voices in animated classics like *Cinderella* and *Sleeping Beauty*, performs the audio for Leota instead. Since she was the voice of Maleficent and Lady Tremaine, menacing was her specialty, a skill your Ghost Host respects.

The first version of floating head trick involved the a looped projection of Leota's face on a vanilla head inside a crystal ball, somewhat similar to the Hatbox Ghost of today. Since more distance existed between the Doombuggy track and the crystal ball, track lighting never disrupted the effect. Clever theme park tourists noticed a glare from the projector into the ball, though.

Currently, Disney uses a kind of green-screen system to create the illusion of a floating crystal ball. Their HD video rear projection builds Leota's face directly from inside her head. This tactic works better than projection from a different spot since it removes the reflection issue.

And there you have it. Those are the tricks of the trade that make my home the swingiest joint in the afterlife...but before you go, there's a little matter I forgot to mention. Beware of hitchhiking ghosts! They have selected you to fill our quota, and they'll haunt you until you return! Now I will raise the safety bar, and a ghost will follow you home!

CHAPTER EIGHT

SPACE MOUNTAIN

Space Mountain is the alpha and omega of Disney roller coasters. Its legendary status is so significant that it's a pop culture reference virtually everyone understands. Perhaps no other theme park attraction in the history of the industry has better name recognition. How does the attraction pull off all the tricks that have made it such a theme park behemoth? Let's go behind the ride to find out all the dazzling secrets of Space Mountain.

THE EXPERIENCE

The original indoor roller coaster

THE TRICK

An idea literally a decade in the making

Here are three facts about the design of Space Mountain:

- Space Mountain debuted in 1975.
- Walt Disney helped to plan Space Mountain.
- Walt Disney died in 1966.

The above reflects just how much planning was involving in the building of the world's first indoor roller coaster. Disney employees at WED Enterprises loved space travel, one of the most popular subjects of the 1950s and 1960s. Their job duties occasionally allowed them to interact with the heavyweights of the field. Disney even aired "science factual" programming during the 1950s that used Wernher von Braun, the father of Rocket Science, as a technical advisor.

Nobody cared more about getting the science of space travel right more than Walt Disney. When his cohorts presented plans for a space travel simulator called Space Port, he loved the idea. Walt financed concept art for the attraction and even argued for a critical component of its design. He believed that Space Port would only work as a dark ride—an indoor dark ride.

Constructing an outdoor re-creation of outer space wasn't ideal to Disney. He knew that sunlight and inclement weather were both factors that could disrupt the illusion of interstellar travel. An indoor setting would provide a controlled environment, a better backdrop for the emptiness of outer space. Imagineers could paint the walls and control the lighting, re-creating the unforgettable imagery of mankind's first escape from its atmosphere. While Neil Armstrong's walk on the moon was still several years away, scientists already knew the mechanics of orbital launch. Innovators such as Wernher von Braun could provide Disney with advice on building the most realistic Space Port.

There was just one problem...

THE EXPERIENCE

A steel roller coaster system with a satisfyingly bumpy ride

THE TRICK

Computer relay systems

Disneyland wasn't the place where Space Mountain debuted. Instead, it became the first truly new ride in the history of Magic Kingdom. Almost everything else there was a re-creation of something already existing at Disneyland. The lone exception wasn't a ride but instead an audio-animatronic show, Country Bear Jamboree. Why did a ride Walt Disney worked on get delayed until nine years after his death?

Imagineers honed in on an emerging technology of the 1960s. At the time, business computers were literally as big as an office floor, and their processing power was inferior to a Commodore 64. Disney knew that they wanted computer controllers to pick and choose the times when coaster carts were supposed to leave the departure area. They had a similar idea in place to the way that air traffic control worked at the time. Unfortunately, technology hadn't caught up with them yet. The hardware required to build what they were now calling Space Mountain didn't exist yet. Even if it had, Disney would have found the prices exorbitant and prohibitive.

The company had no choice but to wait for computers to grow more powerful. Walt Disney unfortunately didn't live long enough to see his dream of indoor space travel come to fruition. In his absence, Walt Disney World became a reality, but Space Mountain wasn't one of the original rides. The attraction wouldn't open for another several years. Part of it was the economics of opening a new theme park. Most of it was that the technology still needed improvement.

By 1972, Disney projected that they'd soon have the computing power needed to build an indoor, fully automated roller coaster. So, they spent a couple of years building a mountain, one carefully measured so as to avoid outshining Cinderella Castle, and they waited for the strongest computer technology available.

In 1974, Disney implemented a control system that decides when roller coaster carts leave the station as well as when they return. The power of these computer sensors was so impressive for the 1970s that they could recognize when a cart was out of position and automatically shut down the ride. It was a hallmark achievement in ride safety and perhaps the first vision of Walt's Experimental Prototype City of Tomorrow.

Space Mountain took all the danger out of its ride system by removing cast members from the equation. Its computers track every movement of all 30 carts in operation, guaranteeing that collisions never occur. This might not sound like a huge deal today, but in 1975, it wasn't just state-of-the-art technology. It was revolutionary theme park design that was years ahead of its time.

THE EXPERIENCE

Interstellar travel in the span of three minutes

THE TRICK

a slow ride back to Earth

The genius of Space Mountain is its dizzying experience. Because the coaster cart hurls guests into the great unknown of outer space, they quickly lose a sense of ordinary Earth standards. The perception of Space Mountain is that it's a frenzied, kinetic coaster that travels at intergalactic speeds. The truth is shocking.

The maximum velocity for the original version of Space Mountain at Magic Kingdom is 35 miles per hour. In execution, it travels even slower, going 28 miles per hour most of the time. For perspective, Seven Dwarfs Mine Train, an attraction critics assail for its gentility, goes 34 miles per hour. Why does it feel so soft whereas Space Mountain seems so frenetic?

In execution, Space Mountain is a glorified experiment in sensory deprivation. The rider starts in a room full of bright lights pulsating as they count down to liftoff. Once the cart explodes into motion from its resting position, the rider is suddenly thrust into the empty darkness of space. They're like Sandra Bullock's character in Gravity, alone in the void of outer space. All known sensations of Earth and gravity fall away into nothingness as the person becomes a space traveler for 150 feverish seconds.

Disney Imagineers specifically chose this type of disruptive ride experience. Space Mountain is supposed to mimic a traveler's return to Earth from a galaxy that may or may not be far, far away (although the similarity is unintentional since Star Wars was still three years away from reality when the attraction debuted). The trip back home is a bumpy ride, with the presumption that if air travel involves turbulence, intergalactic travel is rougher than a Rugby scrum.

The key is the setting. With a darkened interior and an indoor setting, Disney controls all light. They can trigger a sensory response any time they add a new sensation into the void of darkness. All sounds, flurries of lights, and whistling sensations of air snap the rider out of their empty isolation.

In the classic science fiction vernacular, Disney controls the horizontal and the vertical. The person in the ride cart is completely at their mercy, making Space Mountain a controlled environment where the rider is wholly at the mercy of the track in front of them. It was a revolutionary design for the early 1970s, and its underlying psychology continues to drive theme park innovation to this day. Space Mountain earned its reputation as one of the seminal theme park attractions of all-time. Its impact is profound, and it still offers a kickass ride experience almost half a century later.

CHAPTER NINE

BIG THUNDER MOUNTAIN RAILROAD

Never mine for gold on an ancient Indian ground. It's Horror Movie 101. Somehow, the employees of Big Thunder Mining Company never got the memo, probably because the company's owner, Barnabas T. Bullion, is pig-headed and entitled. His stubbornness causes an entire town to pay the price. Let's go behind the ride to figure out where everything went wrong for the unfortunate souls who once lived at Big Thunder Mountain Railroad.

THE EXPERIENCE

Twin man-made mountains thousands of miles apart

THE TRICK

Picking an anti-pirate ride and building a mountain for it

In some alterative timeline, you'd never ride Big Thunder Mountain Railroad. Instead, you'd take a journey on Western River Expedition, which Imagineers projected as the Magic Kingdom response to Pirates of the Caribbean. Remember that the original plans for Walt Disney World oddly didn't feature the globally renowned attraction. Once guests clamored for it, Disney adapted.

During this chaotic time that lasted several years, Imagineer Tony Baxter developed a different ride concept. He pitched a mine train ride that could solve two issues at once. At Disneyland, an attraction called Mine Train Through Nature's Wonderland had collapsed in popularity to the point that park planners downgraded it from E ticket to D ticket. Disney could repurpose this land for a mine train attraction.

At Magic Kingdom, the park had an open space in desperate need of an attraction. They'd intentionally not filled in the area around Frontierland in anticipation of later development. A man-made mountain would ably fill this void. The early designs for Big Thunder Mountain Railroad could satisfy pressing needs at Disney's only two theme parks at the time.

Since Disneyland had a head start, the ride was fast-tracked and opened there first. This park already had developed the space, whereas Magic Kingdom started from scratch. Baxter took inspiration from several locations, most notably Bryce Canyon, Utah. He wanted to create a western-themed attraction with a mix of mountainous terrain and landscaping style.

Baxter and his team built a masterful man-made mountain at Magic Kingdom. They didn't use rock formations exclusively, either. When you look at the façade, you're seeing 6,500 tons of steel, 4,000 gallons of paint, and 4,675 tons of a special mud Disney crafted just for this. There are also 90,000 gallons of water circulating throughout the area. It's an impressive structure that soars 104 feet in the air.

THE EXPERIENCE

A ghost town that feels like people used to live there

THE TRICK

Creating an immersive experience through theming

Building the mountain represented step one of Big Thunder Mountain Railroad. Populating the area with the right items would make it feel lived in. That concept is critical to the runaway roller coaster attraction. The underlying premise of the ride is remarkably deep and nuanced.

The setting here is the 19th century gold rush. The idea is that everyone loses their mind when money is involved. While the various versions of Big Thunder Mountain Railroad all have distinct settings—Disneyland's town is Rainbow Ridge while Magic Kingdom is Tumbleweed—they share a commonality. Someone discovered that there is gold in them thar hills, and they want to mine it. The problem is that the mountain hosting the gold is super-duper-mega cursed. Anyone who tries to take loot winds up regretting it.

An industrialist named Barnabas T. Bullion has a symbolic name that he feels entitles him to all gold on the planet. He sends a team of gold diggers to Big Thunder Mountain to mine its treasures. This causes a dramatic act of God—earthquake at Disneyland, flash flood at Magic Kingdom—to wipe out the town in the middle of the mining process. The space is now an abandoned ghost town that still shows all the signs of its previous business enterprise.

To create the illusion, Baxter and his team sought items that someone would find at a mining excavation. Some of the antiques that you see are fake. Disney has stressed them to add the perception of aged goods. Others are quite real.

Miners required ore for many of their details during the gold rush. In the attraction area, you may notice an ore-hauling wagon and an ore crusher. There's even an old ball mill, something miners used during the process of extracting gold from ore. And yes, Disney used some gold to fortify the walls. It's an authentic touch for a goldminer's town.

The process of ghosting the town was a bit more difficult. How would an Imagineer build a place that looks lived in while simultaneously altering the appearance so that it's later abandoned? Disney used some simple but impressively effective effects for this bit of immersion. They have lanterns that swing as if pushed by some unseen force. They also have ride carts occasionally make the run without riders, a nod to the fact that the runaway train is leaving with or without people on it.

THE EXPERIENCE

A runaway railroad cart through a ghost town

THE TRICK

Building the ricketiest ride in Disney history

Imagineers faced another odd challenge in constructing the railroad. They were building mirror attractions at Disneyland and Magic Kingdom, and the process occurred at almost the same time. The Happiest Place on Earth faced constraints that Walt Disney World didn't have, though.

Everyone knows that space is at a premium at Disneyland. With Big Thunder Mountain Railroad, it was going somewhere that had already had development done. There were non-negotiable space limits in place. Magic Kingdom was the exact opposite. Nothing was there, which meant the ride could be as big as Disney wanted.

Much has been made of the fact that the first two versions were carbon copies. The difference is that Magic Kingdom is 25 percent bigger. That's why it's a longer and generally better ride. In building the coaster tracks i.e. the railroad tracks, Imagineers had to allow for both sizes, and that caused difficulties in building each ride to a crescendo. One goes faster than the other and has more track available. Ergo, it's a different ride experience.

Disney solved this problem by doing something that's anathema now. They built a slower ride cart. Even today, Big Thunder Mountain Railroad maxes out at 35 miles per hour. It's not an attraction built for speed demons. Instead, it's a cerebral ride experience.

What should you feel like as you ride a runaway mine cart? The journey would seem chaotic, and you'd feel completely out of control the whole time, right? Imagineers deduced that they could build that sensation into the ride simply by adding the right bells and whistles to the coaster cart and tracks.

The tracks have steep turns and plenty of dips and hills. You're sending gold down from a mountain, after all. Disney's thought of everything on the ride, as some of the turns happen due to track switches. You'll hear several sounds that emphasize the runaway train theme throughout the ride, too.

Speakers pipe in sounds like bleating goats, squealing brakes, and train whistlers. They even use steam at certain intervals to remind you of transportation system in place. It's precise theming that leads to suspension of disbelief. Each rickety noise causes you to believe that you're tick-tick-ticking your way up the mountain, and the train track helixes demonstrate that you have no control over where your cart is going.

THE EXPERIENCE

Reinvigorating the story with a spectacular line queue

THE TRICK

Creating a new line queue that plusses the ride anew

Disney plussed the Magic Kingdom version of Big Thunder Mountain Railroad, modernizing the line queue with more immersive features. In the process, they enhanced the backstory of the ride, emphasizing Barnabas T. Bullion. A painting on one of the walls depicts the gold magnate as a Tony Baxter clone, a fitting tribute to the Imagineer responsible for the attraction.

In the line queue, you'll notice several elements that enhance your appreciation of the mountain. Perhaps the most exciting one involves a plunger and a lot of dynamite. You'll see crates with explosive warnings at several intervals.

Eventually, you'll reach a point where you can turn a crank. Once you've done so for an appropriate length of time, you can do something that you've only seen in the movies. You can push down a plunger and trigger an explosion! Disney's set up a clever bit of Imagineering outside. When you hit the detonator, a puff of dusty smoke will explode into the sky, just like in so many Westerns!

Other line elements that add to the theming include a bank teller and an open safety vault that has stacks of gold bullions. There's even a painting of the fateful storm that triggered the flash flood that wiped out Tumbleweed.

Another much-appreciated touch is the ventilation system, which you know as the giant fans that cool you down during a hot park day. These are an integral part of the mining infrastructure, as a town blueprint verifies. You can examine all of the places where the ventilation shafts are in place, all while relishing in the welcome breeze.

Finally, alert guests will see one of the least appreciated portions of the line queue. One of the displays hides an interior monitor. On this monitor, several silent movies are available to watch in succession. I must admit that I had to go through the line several times before I paid any attention to the Subterrascope. It's these special touches that have turned an already-spectacular ride into a modern miracle of Imagineering.

CHAPTER TEN

SPACESHIP EARTH

Everyone has a favorite Disney attraction. Mine is Spaceship Earth. Yes, I recognize that it's an unconventional choice, but I've loved it since the first time I rode it back in 1983, the first year of Epcot. Only in recent years have I appreciated its greatness, though. Today, I'd like to take you behind the ride to explain why Spaceship Earth is the most important component of Epcot as a theme park and a concept.

THE EXPERIENCE

The most iconic visual at Epcot

THE TRICK

Following the teachings of a relatively obscure author

You may not know who R. Buckminster Fuller is, but you appreciate his creations just the same. Fuller's impact on Epcot is as dramatic as anyone not named Walt Disney. He popularized and patented the concept of the geodesic dome. You know it as the giant golf ball that sits at the front of Epcot. This creation is an architectural marvel...but not for the reason you think.

Sure, the Epcot ball known as Spaceship Earth is amazing to behold. It's one of the two most important weenies at Walt Disney World, alongside Cinderella Castle. What it represents is even more important. Fuller's teaching is that planet Earth is a spaceship flying through space, and all its residents are astronauts. So, you can brag to your friends that you're an astronaut!

Fuller enumerated the ways that our spaceship has limited resources. He also believed that mankind needed to find new, stronger constructs to build more efficient civilizations. One of those ideas is the geodesic dome, a concept he didn't invent but did bring to the attention of American designers.

The genius of the geodesic dome is that its core is strong. Its "lattice-shell" design can sustain heavy loads. Spaceship Earth kills two birds with one stone for Disney. It's the weenie that everyone knows by sight, even people who have never visited Walt Disney World. As a happy bonus, it's symbolic of conservation and our societal need to work together, two of the underlying themes of Epcot. And Fuller was even kind enough to give the structure its name!

THE EXPERIENCE
Building a geodesic dome

THE TRICK
Breaking one big thing into 11,324 little pieces

Of course, all of these comments are theoretical. Building the geodesic dome is where the real work happened. Spaceship Earth was a 26-month project that required six pylons buried between 120 and 185 feet into the ground to secure the foundation plus 1,700 tons of steel for dome itself. The outer surface of the structure is roughly 150,000 square feet, and the panels of it are known as alucobond. Disney uses this substance due to its mirroring effects. Alucobond shows guests below during the day and accentuates the sparkling lights of other park elements at night.

Spaceship Earth has 11,324 alucobond-based panels that give the building both its ability to support heavy weights and its novel appearance. These panels are also nearly indestructible and weather-resistant, both of which are important traits in hurricane-prone Central Florida. Spaceship Earth was by no means the first geodesic dome but even 35+ years after its creation, it remains the most famous one.

THE EXPERIENCE
Displaying seminal moments in history via elegant set pieces

THE TRICK
Using lifelike audio-animatronics to re-create history

The most important parts of Spaceship Earth the attraction are the set pieces. Yes, this statement is true of many Disney attractions, as Walt Disney taught his team to build rides the same way that they illustrated movies. Most attractions compartmentalize cleanly into distinct phases. It's particularly true of Spaceship Earth, though.

Since the space is so large (its dimensions are 50 meters by 55 meters with 2.2 million cubic feet in volume), these set pieces are among the biggest ever made for a Disney attraction. They must demonstrate grandeur in scale, particularly where the ball is at its widest. The wall projections for two of the scenes are done by necessity inasmuch as out of inspiration.

When Disney cannot project wooly mammoths or images of Earth from above, they use audio-animatronics (AAs) as lifelike re-creations of important historical figures. Spaceship Earth features more than 50 of these robotic humans to tell several stories. Guests have developed favorites over the years such as the computer lab technician, the printing press owner, and the ancient teachers. Each one highlights an amazing set piece that tells a story with little to no dialogue. The accessories in each section disseminate the information.

Sometimes, Disney even repurposes existing AAs. Riders who pay careful attention will note that some of the AAs bear a striking resemblance to American presidents! It's not your imagination. Disney has transferred a few AAs from Hall of Presidents to populate some of the scenes in inexpensive fashion. Teddy Roosevelt, John Adams, and Andrew Jackson are on display. When they're not playing presidents, they're a Roman Senator, a writing monk, and a Gutenberg printer worker.

THE EXPERIENCE

Relaying seminal moments in history as consumable parcels

THE TRICK

Keeping the dialogue fresh with Dame Judi Dench

While the set pieces largely lack dialogue, Disney's always employed a narrator to tie the experience together. In the earliest days, Vic Perrin explained the history of mankind as shown on the ride. You may not know who he is, but his casting made perfect sense at the time. He was Control Voice on The

Outer Limits, which means he handled one of the seminal audio clips of the 1960s.

Perrin's role at Spaceship Earth lasted four years. There was nothing wrong with his performance. Park planners simply decided that they wanted someone with more stature. They chose news anchor Walter Cronkite. Disney also added a cheesy song called "Tomorrow's Child" to accompany the ride.

I believe that this move distracted from the presence of Cronkite, one of the most trusted voices in broadcasting, but it's a minor gripe. The important aspect is that Disney viewed Spaceship Earth as the signature attraction at Epcot. They updated it only four years after the park's opening, changing the later section to reflect the new theme of "Tomorrow's Child." They altered it again multiple times over the next several years.

One of those changes was to swap out Cronkite for Jeremy Irons in 1994. A dozen years after Spaceship Earth's debut, Disney added a dozen new scenes, making the entire ride feel reborn. They also eliminated the "Tomorrow's Child" portion, accepting that it hadn't worked quite as well as intended.

Irons maintained his role for 13 years, making him the current holder of the longest tenure title on Spaceship Earth. In 2007, Disney replaced him with the current narrator, Dame Judi Dench. They also altered several scenes and added new ones. Most importantly, Disney...well, we'll get to that in the next section.

The purpose of Dench, Irons, Cronkite, and Perrin has always been the same. The narration fills in the space between the set pieces. Disney can explain the importance of each sequence without boring the audience. It makes each standalone story feel like part of a larger tapestry, the evolution of humankind throughout history.

THE EXPERIENCE

Choosing your own adventure in the future

THE TRICK

Upgrading tech to make the ride down as engaging as the ride up

With the 2007 update, Disney finally found the perfect ending for the attraction, the downward phase that's always been problematic. Imagineers added an element that gamified this section. They did so to honor the new sponsor of Spaceship Earth, a forward-thinking corporation named Siemens, who came onboard in 2005. While the sponsorship ended in 2017, the ideas from it remain fruitful to this day.

On the current iteration of the ride, you can use a touchscreen to choose a few aspects of your future life. Once you've completed the interactive questionnaire, Spaceship Earth produces an adorable animated video that displays a better tomorrow, one where technology makes your life easier.

The "choose your own adventure" portion is the missing element that this attraction always needed to exemplify all phases of the Epcot dream. Now, the ride starts with a visual, informational section before segueing into an optimistic take on life a few years from now. It's the perfect mix of understanding yesterday while looking forward to tomorrow, precisely what Walt Disney did when he announced the Experimental Prototype Community of Tomorrow more than half a century ago!

CHAPTER ELEVEN

STAR TOURS: THE ADVENTURES CONTINUE

On May 20, 2011, Disney's Hollywood Studios became the first of three Disney theme parks (so far) to host an updated version of arguably the most iconic motion simulator ride in existence.

Star Tours: The Adventures Continue (aka Star Tours II) replaced the original Star Tours attraction that (officially) debuted on January 9, 1987. The debut of the updated Star Tours represented the culmination of roughly 13 years of work by Disney Imagineers. These cast members had spent the entirety of the Star Wars prequel trilogy years planning how to incorporate the new movie ideas into a better ride simulation. Let's go behind the ride to determine exactly what was changed and what steps were required to achieve one of the most impressive and unprecedented rides, even to this day.

THE EXPERIENCE

Updating a 3D simulation of a Star Wars vacation gone awry

THE TRICK

Over a decade of planning and a new third dimension

The origin of the first iteration of Star Tours is mundane. *Star Wars* creator George Lucas asked what Disney's Imagineers were working on when he visited. They said that they were building a new flight simulator. He asked for ideas on how to implement a similar ride with Star Wars characters. Two years later, they gave him a collated list. The rest is theme park history.

In 1986, the parties began to build an unforgettable attraction bearing both the Star Wars and Disney brands, a union that would pay dramatic dividends a couple of decades later. The new attraction known as Star Tours came with a price tag of $32 million, but its instant popularity was unmistakable.

Disneyland operated for 60 straight hours to handle the immediate, constant demand for their new signature motion simulator.

Approximately a decade later, the old version had grown stale, and consumers often requested an update. In 1998, Lucas' people contacted Disney to say that he was working on *Episode One* and knew the sequence that should become the backbone of Star Tours II. The scene in question was the Pod Race, and he was correct that it was a worthy follow-up as a ride experience.

Disney sketched out the attraction update as this one story, presuming the Pod Race would comprise the totality of Star Tours II. In 1998, they'd decided to make the ride in 3D with glasses similar to Anakin's. They wanted to tether the ride to the planned Star Wars prequel. They had no idea at the time that the film itself would break the hearts of many moviegoers.

Alas, fortune was in their favor. Nothing happened with the actual design of the ride until October 2003. Since the Imagineers had no advance knowledge of what would be in *Episode 2* or *Episode 3*, they eventually decided to wait until the new trilogy ended. After their release, however, Disney's employees couldn't pick their favorite sequence from these films, either. They knew that for Star Tours II to surpass its grandiose expectations, more oomph was needed.

THE EXPERIENCE

54 different variations of the same ride

THE TRICK

A storytelling slot machine

Have you heard of the *Choose Your Own Adventure* books by Packard and Montgomery? Disney's Imagineers recognize that *Star Wars* was a global phenomenon and that its fans hungered for an original experience that would allow them to enjoy multiple visits into the fertile imagination of George Lucas. The designers settled upon a "storytelling slot machine" premise.

Their pitch to Lucas involved a five-part story of a take-off sequence for a ship, a journey to a new land, a detour caused by shenanigans, a transition away from this area, and a main event that would comprise the body of the ride time. The trick was revolutionary for the time and remains novel today.

There is a random calculation made to determine which of multiple options each ride will employ. The initial pitch called for four possibilities on take-off, six on the travel segment, 12 on the detour, an undetermined amount for the transition, and another dozen for the main event. As originally envisioned, the ride would have offered at least 3,456 potential variations and somewhere around 13,824, presuming that there were at least as many transition possibilities as take-off segments.

Alas, such lofty ambitions demanded too much legwork for the time. As it was, Star Tours II required new 3D as well as digital technologies, neither of which was well established during the design phase. Filming another 30-34 potential ride mechanics would have taken far too much time. They eventually settled upon providing enough random variations to offer 54 permutations of Star Tours: The Adventure continues. That's 53 more than virtually any other ride on the planet.

Later, the arrival of a new batch of Disney-owned and distributed Star Wars releases would change the calculus. Starting with *Star Wars: Episode VII—The Force Awakens*, Star Tours II became more like Star Tours II.5. Imagineers introduced some of the sequences from the new movies into the ride possibilities. BB-8 became one of the messengers, as an example.

The modern version of Star Tours: The Adventures Continue has come with several different permutations. For a time, all versions of the ride started on Jakuu, the base planet from *The Force Awakens*. When *Rogue One: A Star Wars Story* entered theaters, Disney returned to variable starting locations.

This sort of sequencing modification has happened each time that there's a new Star Wars movie. In this way, Star Tours II delivers a new ride experience more often than any other Disney attraction. How do they do it? Well...

THE EXPERIENCE

Authentically re-creating parts of the *Star Wars* universe

THE TRICK

Picking the right combination of *Star Wars* favorites

Imagineers faced a new problem after narrowing their focus to the appropriate number of ride options. They needed to pick the correct ones. The designers presented George Lucas with a story matrix for Star Tours II. It is largely the one in use today.

This version of the story matrix offers two options during the introduction, an encounter with Darth Vader and Storm Troopers or an explosive situation with Han Solo. Then, it randomizes a trip to Tattooine, Hoth or Kashyyyk. If you're not familiar with Kashyyyk, it's also known as Wookiee World.

The implementation of Kashyyyk is particularly fun for Imagineers, because it's a creation of a world that is largely not seen in the films. So, they had more freedom with it than with the well-established planets of Tattooine and Hoth.

After you reach one of the three planets, you may interact with Yoda, Admiral Ackbar, or Princess Leia, creating a total of nine divergent branches for the ride during this phase. Two of those encounters go better than the other one.

Finally, you travel to either Coruscant, Naboo, or the Death Star. So, in a perfect world, you run into Darth Vader, decipher the backwards talk of Yoda, and narrowly escape a Death Star. If everything goes wrong, you meet Storm Trooper flunkies, look at Ackbar's HD-unfriendly face, and avoid thinking of the quote, "Hold me like you did by the lake on Naboo," as you exit the ride. The sheer volume of possibilities is remarkable.

Disney later updated Star Tours: The Adventures Continue for the Disney era of Lucasfilm ownership. They added two new possibilities in the first segment, although they're only slight modifications of previous encounters. Now, instead of Darth Vader, guests sometimes run into Kylo Ren. And instead of Han Solo, you might see Rey instead.

During the second stage, Jakku is a new destination. The short third stage has the largest number of additions. BB-8, Poe Dameron, and Maz Kanata are all possibilities in the coordinates sequence. It's a small change, but it doubles the theoretical number of Star Tours permutations.

Finally, the last stage adds one new option, Crait. You'll add Poe against the First Order here. And the fitting part is that your cruiser shuts down on Batuu. Disney fans are smiling right now, as they appreciate that it's the home world for Star Wars: Galaxy's Edge, the spectacular themed land at Disney's Hollywood Studios and Disneyland.

THE EXPERIENCE
Filming new Star Wars moments

THE TRICK
Trusting the wizardry of Team Lucas

Disney employees met with Lucas every three weeks, a stark contrast to the first version where Lucas only participated in only a handful of meetings. His input paid particular dividends with regards to making the ride more user-friendly.

The *Star Wars* creator queried Imagineers about whether a person could participate more directly in the ride. He suggested that the ride capture an image of a random guest, enabling them to become part of a story by getting inserted into the movie. It's the dream of so many *Star Wars* fans to become a part of the universe, and they can do just that in Star Tours II directly thanks to Lucas' suggestion.

Of course, there was a lot more to developing the ride than this. Disney had to film key scenes in order to create new action sequences. Stunt people in costumes brought to life the new ideas from the Star Tours II script.

My favorite is that there is video of a Wookiee hitting a windshield, as shown on the set. At some developer conferences, Imagineers display it to help the viewer understand what it looks like when a guy in a glorified cosplay outfit charges at a camera during principal photography. It's utterly ridiculous to watch. Then, they reveal the same effect as how it looks during The Adventure Continues thanks to a bit of film magic.

Every second of original *Star Wars* footage is examined as carefully as the Zapruder Film. The fact that Disney received authorization to film this much Star Wars footage with the blessing of George Lucas is a tremendous feat. At least, it was before Disney wrote Mr. Lucas a check for $4 billion and bought Lucasfilm for themselves.

THE EXPERIENCE
Crafting a better pre-show

THE TRICK
Enhancing and evolving an established classic

The invention of the FastPass caused some frustration for Imagineers. The original design of Star Tours was predicated upon show times. Each ride kept to a specific schedule. So, they could control the amount of time needed for pre-show interactions with Star Tours. Once FastPasses changed all that, some park guests found themselves waiting in line for more than 10 minutes, a longer period than anticipated by Imagineers.

With Star Tours: The Adventures Continue, Disney employees took a more forward thinking approach. They planned for extended visitation time in the pre-show, understanding that even if guests were stuck there for an hour, entertainment options should distract them for a lot of the time. In order to achieve this goal, they went back to basics.

The core concept of Star Tours is that it's the *Star Wars* universe's equivalent to an airport. It's a launching pad to any tourist destination in existence. What changed in terms of airport travel in the interim between Star Tours and Star Tours II? Security. So, some of the old favorites from the first iteration such as G2-9T and G2-4T, previously worker droids, transferred over as security bots.

Since the Lucas-founded Industrial Light & Magic always enjoys original opportunities to play in the sandbox, they too got involved. As usual, they also overachieved. Pay attention to their little touches throughout the pre-show area. For instance, note the droids in charge of windshield wiping. They need instructions on the best way to proceed. Since ILM had an internal debate about this, they offered several versions, all of which are incorporated into the pre-show functionality. It's almost a prelude to the multitude of random events in The Adventure Continues itself.

THE EXPERIENCE

New music and a new but familiar pilot

THE TRICK

Adding two iconic Star Wars celebrities

Along those lines, a different pilot was requested as a dramatic change from skittish Rex as voiced by Pee Wee Herman in Star Tours. A gung-ho pilot named Ace was intended to replace him as captain. There was even a competition among Imagineers to come up with the winning look for Ace.

All of that creative conflict was rendered irrelevant when Lucas suggested that the stark contrast between Ace and Rex was too dramatic. He determined that Disney should unearth another option to captain the ship.

One was right under everyone's nose. An employee had the epiphany that nervous flights were kind of C-3PO's thing, and Lucas adored the idea. So, a beloved *Star Wars* droid was incorporated in lieu of a new character. Imagineers loved their creation, Ace, so much that it is a pre-show staple.

The other major change was sound quality. Composer John Williams let people know that he was a huge fan of the ride. He told Lucas and Lucas told Disney, who was thrilled to hire him. It was the first time Williams ever worked with Disney.

In addition, composer Michael Giacchino is also a huge fan of *Star Wars*. Disney executives happily hired the man who is only a Tony away from an EGOT (Emmy, Grammy, Oscar, and Tony award). He asked to handle the pre-show and then created what he describes as travelogue versions of many classic *Star Wars* sounds.

Try to listen to some of these greatest hits during the hectic, loud pre-show sequence. With Williams and Giacchino handling the sounds, The Adventures Continue makes the audio in the original Star Tours sound like an eight-bit videogame.

One final touch in the pre-show is something you can explore during your ride wait. There are several hidden enhancements placed in plain sight for the alert guest.

These knickknacks include some of WALL-E's prized possessions, some of Captain EO's robots, a representation of Madame Leota, audio shout-outs to people such as Lucas, his film THX 1138, a Disney fireworks show, a hidden Mickey (natch), and even a competing movie universe's Starship Enterprise.

The best enhancement of all is subtle, though. There is an image of a carbonite prison slab containing Jar Jar Binks, fulfilling the dream of yousa and meesa.

CHAPTER TWELVE

SPLASH MOUNTAIN

Song of the South is the most controversial semi-animated film ever produced by Walt Disney. It's also one of the few that Walt chose not to release under his own umbrella, instead choosing RKO Radio Pictures as the distributor for his first movie to include live actors. You almost certainly know of the contentions about *Song of the South*'s shortcomings. That's why the everlasting popularity of the Disney park attraction based on the film is so remarkable. It's able to overcome a negative stigma, warming the hearts of generations of tourists. How does this ride accomplish such an impressive feat? Let's go behind the ride to learn many of the best tricks employed at Splash Mountain.

THE EXPERIENCE

Delayed gratification as an art form

THE TRICK

Heightened anticipation

A lot of Disney visitors are under the impression that Splash Mountain is one of the oldest attractions at Disneyland and Walt Disney World. In truth, it only dates back to 1989 at Anaheim and 1992 at Orlando. When conceptualizing the idea of a ride with a watery landing, Disney's Imagineering team understood that log flume rides with aquatic finishes weren't unusual, even for the late '80s. In order to craft an attraction worthy of the Disney brand, they'd have to differentiate their experience. Even if they achieved that, however, they'd still need to put the splash in Splash Mountain. Otherwise, they'd disappoint and frustrate their guests.

Disney's brilliant park planners deduced that they could enhance the ride simply through a strong visual display. You know the one I mean. The man-made structure of Splash Mountain chases away all the cowards who fear the thought of getting doused with water. Whereas most log flume attractions are fast and to the point, Disney went a different way with Splash Mountain. It uses several false finishes to confuse and delight park visitors. They see the giant drop at the end of the ride as they approach the attraction. Then, the line queue provides several more up-close perspectives of giddy guests suffering the wrath of a tsunami.

The idea is to keep the idea of the final splashdown in the rider's head the entire time they wait in line. Then, theme park tourists used to a straight up then straight down log flume experience will fall for the twist at the first turn. They'll think they're about to receive a face full of water, only to recognize that they've been tricked. It's devious at first, and then Splash Mountain stretches out the gag by doing it several more times. By the time the rider gets to the actual precipitous drop, they're no longer sure what to believe, thereby feeling a different type of surprise when the water bombards them. It's a masterful type of psychological manipulation that Disney employs to euphoric effect. Few first-time riders exit Splash Mountain without a smile on their faces.

THE EXPERIENCE

Celebrating a largely disavowed movie

THE TRICK

Emphasizing the joy via subtle manipulation

If you look for a video release of *Song of the South*, you won't find it. Disney has wisely chosen never to distribute the film due to some...unfortunate aspects. What Disney's programmers learned during the first 20 years of Disneyland surprised them. Some of the characters from Song of the South were among the most popular roaming mascots at the park. Whenever Br'er Bear, Br'er Fox, and Br'er Rabbit walked around Disneyland, a crowd of kids mobbed them. Disney saw an opportunity to redeem them if not the film itself.

Let's ignore the movie's divisiveness for a moment, instead focusing on the Disneyland experience from a child's perspective. They're at the Happiest Place on Earth, the dream destination of anyone who still describes their age with the modifier, "X Years...and a half." When they see a furry bear, fox, or rabbit, what's their natural instinct? Children live in a hugger culture, and fuzzy animals are the cuddliest. You could start an animated series tomorrow with a bear, fox, and rabbit, and you'd immediately have the attention of merchandisers across the land. In other words, Disney boldly chose not to throw the baby out with the bath water when it came to the characters of *Song of the South*.

How could they emphasize the good while glossing over the bad? I would imagine that was the subject of many tense staff meetings during the 1980s. As always, Disney found the answer through anthropomorphic animals. They chose to re-tell the exciting adventures of Brer Rabbit using standard Disney staples: splashy colors and child-friendly set designs. The emphasis of the entire attraction is silliness for the sake of joy.

After the initial swerve of a fake splashdown, the first set piece introduces the rider to Br'er Frog. His primary purpose is to warn of the conflict between Br'er Rabbit and Br'er Fox. This tactic was a brilliant way to place the focus on the attraction and its goofy characters rather than an unfortunate cinematic blemish on Walt Disney's resume. Still, when the time came to re-create the climactic events of the Br'er Rabbit story, Disney chose a beehive full of honey rather than...the other thing.

THE EXPERIENCE

Having Guests Exit with a Smile

THE TRICK

The best musical earworms at Magic Kingdom

For all its flaws, *Song of the South* has a tremendous strength. Did you know that it's an Academy Award-winning film? It's true. Song of the South won in the category of Best Song for "Zip-a-Dee-Doo-Dah," a true Disney classic. That's not the only masterpiece from the soundtrack, though. Disney's Imagineers culled the nine tracks played in the movie, eventually picking the ones they felt would embody the theme of the ride: happiness.

In addition to "Zip-A-Dee-Doo-Dah," the obvious inclusion, Disney added "Ev'rybody's Got a Laughin' Place," "Burrow's Lament" (known as "Sooner or Later" in *Song of the South*), and "How Do You Do" to the attraction. Disney sagely chose to end the ride with the signature song, "Zip-A-Dee-Doo-Dah." I would argue that it's How Do You Do that provides the most lasting impact from Splash Mountain, though. It's a potent earworm.

Imagineers again trigger your emotions through subtle manipulation. The goal here is to keep you smiling throughout the ride. That's why the attraction emphasizes the goofy banjo music in the scene following "How Do You Do." Your flume is about to take you to the Laughing Place...which isn't as funny a place as you might expect. The surreal aspects of it are palatable since you're still smiling from the prior scene. Then, once it's over, you finally reach the mountain's titular splash. Even that's a false finish, though. The ride isn't quite over. After getting soaked, you've earned your reward: a rambunctious performance of "Zip-A-Dee-Doo-Dah." Disney artfully uses music to control your emotions from the start to finish of the ride.

MISCELLANY

Have you ever wondered why the attraction bears the name of Splash Mountain? The movie includes no mention of such a place. The explanation is shamelessly commercial. Imagineer Tony Baxter coaxed two of his peers, Bruce Gordon and John Stone, into helping him storyboard an attraction he envisioned as Zip-a-Dee River Run. This occurred in 1983, and Disney's executives loved the idea since the new ride would reinvigorate Bear Country, a largely ignored part of Disneyland.

Unfortunately, the project lacked the momentum to begin immediately. Then-CEO Michael Eisner tossed in his support for the ride, albeit with a caveat. He had a new movie to promote, a 1984 release you should know, *Splash*. The Tom Hanks/Daryl Hannah film told the story of a man following in love with a mermaid. Eisner suggested (well, demanded) a name change to Splash Mountain to add synergy to the film. He also requested the inclusion of a mermaid in the attraction. You've never noticed this since attraction wouldn't debut for another five years after the film's release. By that time, a *Splash* tie-in didn't seem relevant, not that it ever was. Still, the name of Splash Mountain stuck.

Also, if you've ever wondered about the presence of the log flume itself, Disney's storytellers have an answer for you. Helpful beavers with especially long teeth carved the boats so that you can enjoy your trip through the bayou. How they glued the wood together is less settled.

Finally, Splash Mountain was one of the most expensive attractions Disney had built up until that point. The detailed set pieces combined with the accompanying man-made mountain caused construction costs to soar. The eventual price tag was $75 million, which is the equivalent of almost $145 million today.

CHAPTER THIRTEEN

THE TWILIGHT ZONE TOWER OF TERROR

"Hollywood, 1939. Amid the glitz and the glitter of a bustling, young movie town at the height of its golden age, The Hollywood Tower Hotel was a star in its own right; a beacon for the show business elite. Now, something is about to happen that will change all that. The time is now on an evening very much like the one we have just witnessed."

What's so perfect about the Twilight Zone Tower of Terror? It's a supernatural attraction that brings a dead man back to life. I'm not even talking about one of the characters in the story. Instead, I'm referencing Rod Serling, the host of the attraction and its namesake television show. He died in 1975, but Disney's Hollywood Studios didn't unveil the ride until 1994. How's that for spooky? In this article, we'll discuss this and several other chilling aspects of the accursed building known as the Hollywood Tower Hotel. Let's go behind the ride to learn why Twilight Zone Tower of Terror is such a classic.

THE EXPERIENCE

Entering the Twilight Zone

THE TRICK

Choosing the perfect IP from several diverse options

What do Mel Brooks and Stephen King have in common? The logical response is, "Not much." For Disney park planners, however, they were candidates on the same drawing board. During the Blue Sky phase of plotting Disney's Hollywood Studios, both of these content creators were in discussion for a new attraction.

Imagineers wanted to build something spooky as part of their movie-based theme park. One of their inspirations was

Young Frankenstein, the Mel Brooks movie. Park officials and then-CEO Michael Eisner met with Brooks about the idea, which would become the first major expansion at Hollywood Studios.

After a time, this idea fell by the wayside, and Disney moved along to the works of Stephen King. This ride concept also would have embraced the supernatural. Disney officials quickly realized that Stephen King wasn't a great match with the land of Mickey Mouse, though.

Eventually, park officials realized that a perfect match was available. *The Twilight Zone* ran for 156 episodes, and its legend had only grown during the new era of cable television programming. After several years of discussion, Hollywood Studios had found its perfect match. The intellectual property (IP) of *The Twilight Zone* was the perfect premise for a ride.

THE EXPERIENCE

Creating a Tower that terrifies

THE TRICK

Classic Disney construction with an ominous twist

Once park planners settled on an IP, they embarked on a strategy to bring *The Twilight Zone* to life. They quickly settled on a classic Hollywood theme for the attraction, recognizing that Imagineers could construct the perfect weenie as a bookend for one side of the park. A Tinseltown hotel, one where A-list celebrities escaped the common people, was the perfect setting for a ride.

The premise checked several boxes at once. The hotel skyscraper would draw attention to Hollywood Studios, even from a distance. There was a catch, though. One side would be visible to guests at Epcot, and the line of sight matched the Mexico Pavilion. It was a potential disruption to the theme of the weenie there, the massive pyramid structure. For this reason, one side of what we now call the Hollywood Tower Hotel has a modest but noticeable Aztec design. Park officials refused to let a new manmade monument disrupt the illusion of an existing one.

There was also the problem of building a giant tower. The underlying premise of the Hollywood Tower Hotel is that it's a skyscraper, one that requires a large elevator shaft to navigate all the floors. As Disney fanatics know, federal regulations stipulate that any structure over 200 feet must have warning lights to signal approaching aircrafts.

Imagineers obeyed these rules, although they pushed the boundaries as much as possible. The hotel is 199 feet tall. For a time, it was the tallest structure at Walt Disney World, although Expedition Everest later surpassed it...by half a foot.

The genius of the Hollywood Tower Hotel is its foreboding, almost menacing presence. This high-rise seems to warn onlookers that they should steer clear of the building. To make it menacing, Disney used a baseline of existing Hollywood hotels such as the Mission Inn and the Biltmore Hotel. Then, they added exterior touches to provide the appearance of disrepair stemming from long-term abandonment. The grave look discourages just as it intrigues, a perfect effect for this attraction.

THE EXPERIENCE

Theming a new building to appear decades old

THE TRICK

Selecting perfect Easter eggs from 156 *Twilight Zone* episodes

Most fans of this ride know that the Imagineers working on it did their homework. They watched all 156 episodes of *The Twilight Zone* during what had to be one of the best work weeks ever. It WAS work, though. Cast members took notes about all of the high points from the series, deciding which elements that they could include at the Hollywood Tower Hotel.

Their shopping list was a weird one. To populate the interior of the hotel, Disney had to acquire plausible items for a hotel lobby. They sought out auction house items at high-profile Los Angeles dealers, ones that would seem right at home in a classic upscale resort. Then, they had to age these items to complete the effect.

Disney trivia buffs know that the last guests at the hotel checked in on October 31, 1939. By the time theme park tourists started visiting again in 1994, it had been abandoned for more than half a century. Everything you see at the hotel is intentionally disheveled, and the theming causes unusual problems for cast members. When they clean up the building, they can't make it TOO clean. That would break the illusion.

The Easter eggs are what make the theming special. Little touches populate the building, especially the Library where a television clip plays. In this room alone, you'll see a Mystic Seer machine, a book entitled "To Serve Man," and glasses that belong to the last man on Earth.

Other classic references include a puppet and a signature. The puppet is from the famous episode, "The Dummy," and the signature shows the name of the person who approved usage of the doomed elevator. That gentleman is Mr. Cadwallader, whom *Twilight Zone* fans know is the Devil. Cheeky touches like this one augment the Tower of Terror experience for those who loved the television series.

THE EXPERIENCE

Bringing the dead back to life

THE TRICK

Using Rod Serling *and* a reasonable approximation

No *Twilight Zone* experience would be complete without the presence of the famed host of the series, Rod Serling. Since he died in 1975, Imagineers faced a unique obstacle. While looking for ideas, they spoke with his widow, Carol Serling.

What Disney wanted to do was bold. Their preferred choice was to show Serling on camera. That's impossible, right? Since you've ridden Tower of Terror, you know that it isn't. You may not understand how it's possible, though.

The next time you're watching the video, pay careful attention to Serling. You'll realize that his onscreen presence is minimal. It's his VOICE that's ubiquitous. Ride designers found the perfect clip for the story that they wanted to tell from an episode entitled It's a Good Life. In that episode, Serling spoke the magic words, so to speak...or at least some of them.

With so much narration ongoing, Imagineers couldn't splice together the entire script. Instead, they used some clever video editing. During Serling's speech, you'll notice that the camera cuts away as he speaks the words "maintenance service elevator." This happens because Serling never uttered those words.

To recite their script, Disney needed someone new, a voice actor capable of imitating Serling perfectly. They underwent an extended casting call before settling on Mark Silverman. His audition earned the approval of Carol Serling, which was good enough for Disney. Much of the dialogue that you hear throughout the attraction is in fact Silverman doing a marvelous impression of Rod Serling rather than Serling himself. You had no idea, did you?

THE EXPERIENCE

A terrifying, unique freefall every time

THE TRICK

Two elevator shafts, a special vehicle, and a brutal drop rate

The true magic of Twilight Zone Tower of Terror is the ride experience. Sure, any theme park could build a basic drop tower. Honestly, most do. Imagineers know this, and it drove them to create the greatest drop tower attraction ever built. They succeeded so well that it's widely considered the best of its kind.

What's so special about Tower of Terror's ride mechanic? The answer is in the design. Park planners knew precisely what they wanted from this ride. All they had to do was do several things that had never been done before to make it happen.

The first step was crafting a pair of elevator shafts. One would carry guests up to the ride area. The other...is more complex. It's the place where you bounce up and down several times. On most drop tower attractions, you fall at such a high rate that gravity ceases to exist for a time.

You can even do a Penny Test to prove this. Drop a penny right as the ride starts. It will "float" in the air since you're moving at the same rate of speed as it is.

Actually, that's not quite true. To achieve the desired effect, Disney hired the most famous elevator company on the planet, Otis Elevator Company, to do something that they'd never done before. Elevator design involves a bit of cushioning, a sort of soothing process wherein the shaft rises at a slower rate to prevent people from freaking out.

Disney wanted the opposite. They needed the fastest possible drop down the elevator shaft. They also wanted a lightning-quick ascension, too. Otis Elevator Company built one of the most expensive elevators ever at Hollywood Studios, and nobody knows it because the elevator sits in the dark most of the time. That blind spot when you're in the drop zone is one of the most violent elevator rides ever built!

You're not even in a free fall during these tense moments. The elevator literally drags you up and down. It's the polar opposite of all other drop zone attractions.

The innovation doesn't stop there, either. You know that moment when it feels like you've escaped the elevator? It's when you ride down a path, seeing *Twilight Zone* spooky sights on the sides. While you're admiring the theming and bracing for the drop, Disney's using unprecedented technology.

To transfer you from one elevator shaft to the other, Imagineers had to create an automated guided vehicle (AGV). It's a mobile elevator cab that can lock and unlock from an elevator. It's also capable of propulsion, which is to say that it can move forward.

Your "elevator" is a technical marvel. First, it carries you up an elevator shaft. Then, it breaks contact with its host and follows a series of hidden sensors down a path. It's a guidance system that safely transports people to the elevator shaft. And its deep functionality enables Disney to play one other trick on riders.

When Twilight Zone Tower of Terror opened, every ride was the same. Later, Disney added a new trick. Using computerized technology and the utility of the AGV, Imagineers realized that they could provide a different ride every time. The number of times that you bounce up and down is a simple, randomized computer calculation. No matter how many times you ride the Tower of Terror, you'll have a different ride experience. It's that final touch of terror that you'll experience in the accursed tower!

CHAPTER FOURTEEN

INDIANA JONES ADVENTURES

Star Tours receives all the hype, but it's not the only Lucasfilm intellectual property (IP) with a presence at a Disney theme park. This attraction casts you in the role of a grizzled archaeologist, one known for a whip, a cocksure grin, and a fedora hat. He's the perfect example of the Adventureland hero. There's just one problem. When Disney built a ride for this man, Henry Walton Jones Jr., he wasn't even a Disney property.

How, then, did a man who chose his pet's name, Indiana, as his moniker become one of the central figures at Adventureland? What was Disney's thought process here, and how authentic is the re-creation of the *Indiana Jones* movie franchise in the attraction? Let's go behind the ride to discover all the secrets and history of Indiana Jones Adventure.

THE HISTORY

While the Walt Disney Company rarely uses outside IP as the backbone of its attractions, it has made exceptions from time to time. *Jeopardy* appeared in the former Ellen's Energy Adventure ride, and *The Twilight Zone* is the only dimension where a Tower of Terror could plausibly exist.

Of course, the first non-Disney ride ever was a cousin to Indiana Jones. Star Tours, based on the *Star Wars* franchise, (officially) arrived at Disneyland in January of 1987. George Lucas, the creator of *Star Wars*, was also the man who imagined Indiana Jones into being. After Disney deftly handled the adaptation of Star Wars into an amusement park attraction, Lucas expressed an interest in their doing the same with Mr. Jones.

This discussion took place all the way back in 1988. It quickly bore fruit, as Disney had just added a new gate at Walt Disney World, Disney-MGM Studios, which we now know as

Disney's Hollywood Studios. Disney wanted a fun celebration of the filmmaking process. When Lucas offered the *Indiana Jones* license, they had the perfect idea. In 1989, the Indiana Jones Epic Stunt Spectacular! arrived, and, with the recent closure of the Great Movie Ride, it's now the oldest remaining Hollywood attraction at the park, although rumors of its impending demise have been around for several years.

What you may not realize is that Indiana Jones Adventure wasn't the first Indiana Jones ride. Yes, construction began on this project in 1989, the same year as the stunt show. The first Indy ride open to the public, however, arrived in 1993 at Disneyland Park in Disneyland Paris. Indiana Jones and the Temple of Peril is a mine cart roller coaster that quickly became one of the anchor selling points at Euro Disney.

For six years, American Imagineers toiled to build a unique attraction at Disneyland's Aventureland. They spent more than $100 million on the project, with one park planner describing the cost as $200 million in 1995. That's the equivalent of $325 million today. Disney spent a lot of money to be in the business of Indiana Jones. What did they get for their money? Read on...

THE EXPERIENCE

An authentic exploration of ancient ruins...in the line queue

THE TRICK

Turning a negative into a positive

Space is perennially tight at Disneyland. Walt Disney himself lamented that he couldn't afford more land when he constructed the park in the middle of former orange groves. In attempting to introduce the Temple of the Forbidden Eye to Adventureland, park planners faced a problem. They had a finite space where they could build what is an extremely large attraction area. It's more than 50,000 square feet in size, most of which is housed in a huge building at the south of campus. And for an added degree of difficulty, Imagineers had to construct the temple so that it didn't interfere with the Disneyland Railroad.

The only way that Disney could fit it in the available space was by positioning it on grounds that aren't technically part of the park. This trick is one that Disney used for the first time 30 years prior to Indiana Jones with the Haunted Mansion. The catch is that for it to work, guests would have to walk about 1,000 extra steps to reach the attraction entrance.

Where most park planners would see obstacles, Imagineers saw a huge opportunity. Guests *have* to walk that path to get to the ride. So, Disney turned the entire area into a mini-themed land inside Adventureland. They added enough trees to create a realistic jungle background, as if the explorer has to navigate through thick foliage to reach the intended destination. Bamboo fences guide the path, and ominous signs hint that the structure ahead is unsafe at best. There are even a few high voltage warnings, an oddity for a derelict temple.

This elongated ride queue has become a staple of the Imagineering toolbox. Expedition Everest takes the same idea and stretches it to the logical extreme by offering artifacts in every square inch of interior line queue. Avatar Flight of Passage has the longest line queue ever built, capable of entertaining guests for three full hours. Many of the conceits of both attractions began with Indiana Jones Adventure and its unavoidable half-mile line queue.

THE EXPERIENCE
Building and populating the Temple of the Forbidden Eye

THE TRICK
Re-creating and expanding the Indiana Jones universe

The origins of this attraction go back so far that *Indiana Jones and the Last Crusade* hadn't even opened yet, much less the one with the aliens and the refrigerator nuke scene. Imagineers could call on only two *Indiana Jones* movies for inspiration in constructing this attraction.

While world-building, they prioritized the hallmarks of an Indiana Jones adventure. Those include a forbidden place where foolhardy explorers have given their lives for countless centuries and a series of set pieces that seem straight from the movies. The latter has always been a particular area of expertise for Imagineers. After all, Walt Disney taught his employees to craft rides as if they were a series of movie sets.

The Temple of the Forbidden Eye lends itself perfectly to that philosophy. The only catch was moving the theme park tourist from set to set, a problem that called for a special solution we'll discuss in the next section.

Building and populating the temple was a fun process. During the 1980s, Indiana Jones was one of the most popular and iconic franchises of the decade. Imagineers were allowed to let their imaginations run wild in creating artifacts that would plausibly exist in an abandoned temple. To ramp up the fear factor, skeletons are ubiquitous. A rumor I can neither confirm nor deny is that the Temple hosts 1,995 skeletons as a wink to the year the attraction opened.

The entirety of the temple is man-made, obviously, but you'll be hard-pressed to think of it in those terms as you ride through the building. The conceit of the attraction is that Indy has unearthed a long-forgotten temple for a goddess named Mara, and intends to find many artifacts that "belong in a museum," as our hero would say.

Mara's nearly omnipotent, and she can grant special powers like eternal life. There's just one catch. You can't look her in the eye, thus the official (but rarely pronounced) name of the attraction, Indiana Jones and the Temple of the Forbidden Eye. The oddity here is that the rider isn't Indiana Jones. Instead, you're trying to help Sallah find his friend, who has gotten lost somewhere in the dilapidated dwelling.

The theming reinforces the idea that if Indy can get trapped here, no regular tourist should ever go inside. The structure itself is impeccable, with a giant ladder leading all the way up to the top of the façade. This isn't a misleading representation of height, either. The "Temple" takes riders across three stories of set pieces. Foreboding elements like a rickety bridge and a hollowed out skull statue offer further hints that guests should turn back the way that they came. It's one of the most realistic jobs of world-building that Disney has ever done, an amazing feat for something that's more than 20 years old. You truly feel like you're stranded in a temple, and you may never see the sun again.

THE EXPERIENCE

A Jeep that carries you back into daylight

THE TRICK

Building a heretofore unknown ride cart called an EMV

The key to the greatness of Indiana Jones Adventure isn't any of the amazing features thus far, though. Instead, it's a ride cart that Imagineers created especially for this attraction.

You already understand the challenges that Disney cast members faced. They had to carry theme park tourists through a giant area covering three floors and tens of thousands of square feet. In the process, they needed a vehicle that accentuated the precarious situation that the riders faced. They were in an abandoned temple and fleeing from an enraged deity, after all.

Disney didn't have this technology available yet, but they did have a kernel of it. Imagineers were always proud of the gimbal-based design of Star Tours. The pivoted support gave the ride unprecedented mobility and the ability to shake riders such that they could "feel" the events happening onscreen. This type of motion simulation was new at the time, and the designers of Indiana Jones deduced that they could use it as the basis for something new.

Enter the Enhanced Motion Vehicle.

Indiana Jones Adventure has a Jeep, only it's not the type of Jeep that you could buy at a store. It's a marvel of engineering that needed several new patents to create. The entire vehicle is a motion simulator, and it can bounce your seat whenever the action dictates an action. When you ride across a creaky bridge, the EMV shakes you so that you appreciate the peril of your predicament.

The technology of the EMV was so revolutionary for the time that Disney had to build a special track to test it. They were understandably nervous about testing an original ride cart on the unsuspecting public. After all, there's a lot that can go wrong. Each EMV is self-sufficient. It has 480 volts of energy to power the vehicle (Disney didn't want an entire fleet of gas-powered vehicles, after all). It also has a durable chassis and actuators that can move the cart in three distinct thrust planes (x, y, and z) and with three different rotational axes (pitch, roll, and yaw). The Disney Jeep seems like it powers the riders at a hefty velocity, but it actually only goes 14 miles per hour. It seems like more due to the bumpy experience and scary supernatural stuff happening all around you.

Disney loved the EMV so much that they used the same technology again for Dinosaur, an Animal Kingdom attraction that uses similar structure. An explorer travels back in time to visit the age of the dinosaurs, only to realize that a comet's about to strike.

Dinosaur opened only three years after Indiana Jones Adventure. Its existence speaks to a rare amount of pride that Imagineers felt about their creation of the EMV. It really is amazing tech. Some rides (mainly at Universal Studios) have a sedentary cart that rocks back and forth but doesn't go anywhere. At Indiana Jones Adventure, the motion simulation is internal, not external. Your seat shakes you until you believe that you are in mortal danger at a forbidden temple.

Indiana Jones Adventure is quietly one of the most influential theme park attractions of the past 30 years. Its impact on motion simulation, ride design, and line queue techniques has revolutionized the industry. The next time you ride it, take a moment to appreciate its influence on Dinosaur, Expedition Everest, Avatar Flight of Passage, and like 15 rides at Universal Studios. It was the precursor to the modern motion simulation style that's so popular today.

CHAPTER FIFTEEN

KILIMANJARO SAFARIS

The bumpy ride convinces you of the realism of the experience. While you've never been on an exotic safari, you cannot shake the feeling that what you're doing is similar. The only difference is that you're perfectly safe in your vehicle. You and your family can gaze in wonder at the natural habitats of countless creatures, all the while knowing that you can leave the park and eat at Disney Springs immediately afterward. How is that even possible? Why, it's Disney magic, of course. Today, let's go behind the ride to explore the attraction that takes you on the wildest adventure of all, Kilimanjaro Safaris.

THE EXPERIENCE

Hosting live animals at a popular theme park

THE TRICK

Keeping Walt Disney's dream alive 30 years after his death

Walt Disney always had a dream for the Happiest Place on Earth. His fervor for creating a destination location for family hangouts led to an amalgam of several popular forms of entertainment. Disneyland featured rides, shows, and other staples of entertainment for that era, up to and including King Arthur Carrousel, an attraction 80 years older than the park that hosts it.

During the planning phase of an iconic attraction, Uncle Walt stated his vision. He wanted to create the most lifelike experience possible at Jungle Cruise, and that meant the ride needed live animals. Disney Imagineers were taken aback by this request. Even the guy who famously replied "can do, can do" didn't see a way to do it, which is why Jungle Cruise has fake animals.

When the company chose to construct Disney's Animal Kingdom, everyone knew that they were fulfilling one of Walt

Disney's greatest wishes. Kilimanjaro Safaris is the logical extension of the premise, the "ride" that carries guests through all the native habitats of the animals that permanently reside at the park. It's the real version of the attraction that was once a glimmer in Uncle Walt's eye as he contemplated Jungle Cruise.

THE EXPERIENCE

Feeling like you're on safari...in the middle of Orlando

THE TRICK

Transforming swampland into habitable land

The building of Animal Kingdom was an exhaustive task. In particular, the "track" for Kilimanjaro Safaris had to be ready at the same time that the park opened. To achieve this goal, Disney had to design countless habitats on what was previously swampland. It wasn't easy. There's a reason that alligators and lions don't hang out a lot, folks. They don't like the same climate and soil.

Disney needed to implement a specific process to build their proverbial Animal Kingdom. First, they had to move 1.5 million cubic yards of dirt, which should make you feel guilty the next time that you complain about raking the yard. The dirt was also spread out over a vast distance, particularly the Kilimanjaro Safaris portion. That park space is 110 acres; the *entirety* of Magic Kingdom is 107 acres. The attraction required this much land to add all the habitats.

Of course, moving the dirt was only the first step. Imagineers then had to introduce vegetation. Otherwise, the animals would never feel at home. Kilimanjaro Safaris brought in 2.3 million bushes, plants, and trees. Even with that much new vegetation, they still faced a problem, though.

THE EXPERIENCE

Seeing animals on the safari

THE TRICK

Clever placement of the salt licks

When Disney created the pathways for the attraction's driving area, they had to guarantee that the animals would stay in sight of the humans on the safari. What would happen if Disney hosted dozens of safaris each hour but the animals didn't visit? It would be the most boring ride ever constructed, not the greatest way to sell a new theme park.

Alas, many of the creatures Disney introduced to the Animal Kingdom habitat are skittish by nature, particularly in the presence of people, who don't have the greatest track record about treating exotic animals well. You're starting to appreciate the scope of the undertaking that is Kilimanjaro Safaris. Despite not being a ride in any conventional sense, it's legitimately in the conversation for most challenging theme park attraction ever built.

Disney attacked the problem in a novel way. They compiled a list of the best zookeepers and animal experts in the world and promptly hired as many as they could. It was an unprecedented compilation of talent, and these behavioral experts developed tricks to lure animals near the tracks. Eagle-eyed theme park tourists can see salt licks, watering holes, hay/grass, and sugar stashes at various points along the safari.

These items are the bait. Without them, the residents of Kilimanjaro Safaris would avoid the vehicle paths. And on hot days, you may notice the residents hanging out at specific rocks. They're fake ones that hide air-conditioning units. The animals have learned which ones keep them cool during the dog days of summer.

THE EXPERIENCE

Populating the Noah's Ark of theme park attractions

THE TRICK

Choosing animals that wouldn't kill each other on sight

For the safari to work perfectly, it needs a wide range of animals. Otherwise, riders would get bored seeing the same species frolic repeatedly. Disney's new zookeepers worked with famous Imagineer Joe Rohde, the project leader, to identify the most fantastic beasts for the safari. They had strange criteria for populating their land with creatures, though.

Disney needed animals that would, in fact, frolic. Sedentary creatures are great for pictures, but they're not good for safari entertainment. Diet and waste processing were other considerations. Some animals eat foods that aren't conveniently available in central Florida, making them impractical residents. Others are messy with their *ahem* food redistribution.

Disney generally preferred more hygienic creatures, although they did make some exceptions. As an example, the elephants are a highlight of the safari, but unlucky cast members have to clean up literally tons of poop each day. Nobody wants that job. Still, Rohde and his team found a way to turn the messes into a positive. The elephant dung gets recycled as fertilizer at other parts of Walt Disney World.

Other factors in choosing animals involved routine and behavior. Some creatures have a tendency to wander, which is the quickest way to get eaten. Disney spent a lot of money importing their animals, and so they needed safeguards in place to prevent unwanted, possibly fatal roaming. Some of the cliffs, trees, and ponds are natural ways that Disney keeps the creatures in their respective habitats. The range also includes electric fences for animals that aren't deterred by the usual hazards.

As for behavior, some critters just don't get along. Zebras are the most famous example, as they have added an unwelcome amount of excitement to Kilimanjaro Safaris. Disney trumpeted the addition of plains zebras in 2012 before removing them a few months later. Their continued presence is a divisive issue because zebras have a tendency to fight one another... or the ride vehicles. Yes, zebras didn't deal with the change and tried to ram a few oversized cars. Disney has since moved them to a different, safer part of the habitat.

THE EXPERIENCE

Kilimanjaro Safaris after dark

THE TRICK

Adding some lights and changing some behaviors

When Animal Kingdom and Kilimanjaro Safaris opened on Earth Day in 1998, critics marveled at the triumphant nature of the ride experience. Guests could see how animals lived, safely and pleasantly. Disney had even negated the natural odors of life on the safari, making the entire fake safari experience less smelly than the real thing. The one regret everyone had was the fact that the ride closed at night.

Imagineers had a reasonable justification for this choice. Many of the animals require special treatments that are difficult to administer in their natural habitats. The zookeepers requested shelters for the caretaking of various creatures. To assure daily health checks, cast members trained their animal charges a special way. They musically signaled each species to head to its assigned overnight residence. A duck call meant it was time for the gazelles to move, the drums triggered an elephant charge, and so forth. It was a nightly exodus from the savannas to the safer parts of the park.

In 2015, Disney finally decided to extend the hours at Animal Kingdom. They simultaneously turned Kilimanjaro Safaris into a dark ride but not the standard Disney kind. Imagineers added lights throughout their human-crafted jungle, which wasn't that hard to do. After all, much of what you see at Kilimanjaro Safaris is already artificial. Many of the structures have concrete bases, but you can't tell due to clever paint jobs and the usual Disney themed touches.

The primary change was in animal behavior. A belief persists that the best time to ride Kilimanjaro Safaris is first thing in the morning when the creatures are up and stirring for the first time. To keep the evening version interesting for riders, Disney had to view their creatures in a new light, figuratively and literally. They had to illuminate the animals in a way that didn't frighten or disrupt the creatures. Also, they had to persuade animals to suddenly change their lifestyles and daily routines.

Ultimately, Disney altered the ride path for the nighttime version of the attraction. Some animals simply weren't going to become nocturnal, even if their zookeepers nudged them down that path. The altered rules for the evening ride reward the animals that are willing to put on a show, though. Disney prevents guests from using flash photography at night, protecting the eyes of its creatures. The drivers compensate for the change by spending more time at each spot, giving riders a better opportunity to spot various creatures in the dark. And the animals get special treats out of feeders as a bonus for staying up past their bedtime.

Given the above, you now understand why Kilimanjaro Safaris is such a hallmark achievement in theme park construction. From swampland, Disney constructed natural habitats for dozens of species. Then, they persuaded these creatures to feel comfortable around humans. Finally, they even convinced a few animals to change their sleeping patterns. It's exactly the sort of Imagineering feat that would have made Walt Disney beam with pride.

CHAPTER SIXTEEN

DINOSAUR

If time travel were easy, everyone would do it. Instead, we're left dreaming of stumbling upon a TARDIS the next time we're in England. Of course, a place in Orlando is home to a time machine, too, and you don't have to be from Gallifrey to ride it. I'm speaking of the CTX Time Rover, the vehicle at Disney's Animal Kingdom that will transport you into the past. To ride it, you'll have to head over to DinoLand U.S.A and get in line for its finest attraction, DINOSAUR. Let's go behind the ride to learn the inner workings of DINOSAUR.

THE EXPERIENCE

Building an amazing ride from a clunker of a movie

THE TRICK

Ignoring the movie and simply emphasizing the amazing

One of the dirty secrets of DINOSAUR is that it's the second dinosaur attraction hosted in its building. When Disney's Animal Kingdom debuted in 1998, it featured a dinosaur ride called Countdown to Extinction. Several of the ideas and innovations discussed here are applicable to both attractions, although I'll specify some key differences along the way.

The most important fact about the change from Countdown to Extinction to DINOSAUR is that then-CEO Michael Eisner loved synergy. When he saw a novel way to market an upcoming Disney animated movie, he embraced the concept. That marketing ploy was the conversion of a still new ride into one simply called DINOSAUR.

The changes that park planners performed were largely cosmetic and family-driven. The original version, Countdown to Extinction, intensified the journey through time. The ride carts jostled theme park tourists, providing them with a better feel for the rough terrain of the era. Since Dinosaur the movie was (theoretically) aimed at children, they calmed the ride carts to make them more appropriate for kids.

Disney didn't create any direct ties to the movie. And the explanation here is quite funny. While Eisner wanted a connection between the film and the attraction, he didn't want to spend extra money for such changes. This odd choice proved fortuitous for Disney, as *Dinosaur* the film was a total bust. DINOSAUR the attraction's lack of a distinct tie-in has allowed it to age gracefully. Otherwise, children would still be asking their parents, "What's the Dinosaur movie?" And those poor parents might feel obliged to watch it.

The closest thing to a link from film to attraction is in a name. *Dinosaur* the movie tells the story of an abandoned Iguanodon named Aladar. In the second version of the ride, the mission is to save an Iguanodon from extinction. Disney's indicated in various news articles that the dinosaur in question IS Aladar, but that's not even explicitly spelled out at any point in the ride. This fact alone tells you how much confidence Eisner and his team had in Dinosaur's theatrical release, which is to say none.

This is the part of the DINOSAUR conversion that fascinates me. Money was especially tight in the wake of Animal Kingdom's opening. Dinosaur the movie was viewed as the most expensive production ever or, at best, 1A to Titanic. Eisner previously had to drop plans for Beastly Kingdom due to budget cuts. If Countdown to Extinction hadn't existed already, there wouldn't be a DINOSAUR today. Eisner never would have expended the requisite funds to start a dinosaur attraction from scratch. We should all be thankful to that dud of a movie for (indirectly) leading to the best version of this attraction.

THE EXPERIENCE

Re-creating the inhabitants of the Cretaceous era

THE TRICK

Populating an entire building full of believable dinosaurs

When Disney Imagineers planned this attraction, they stressed the importance of authenticity. It's a recurring aspect of Disney theming, but DINOSAUR caused particular problems. Dinosaurs are, you know, freakin' huge. Park space at Disney theme parks is limited. Even Disney's Animal Kingdom, the largest of the four gates at Walt Disney World, has space issues.

Imagineers had to think about the roof and the floor when they re-created the Cretaceous era. Sure, they wanted the dinosaurs to have the correct dimensions. Builders had to maintain the structural integrity of the facility, though. To construct dinosaurs of the appropriate height and weight, Disney had to build some of these gigantic beasts straight into the floor of building. Some of these audio-animatronics (AAs) are so massive that they have their own foundations inside the facility.

Perhaps the most famous of the creatures is Dino-Sue. She sits in the exterior courtyard of DINOSAUR, welcoming guests while setting the tone for the attraction. Dino-Sue is Disney's lovingly crafted duplicate of FMNH PR 2081 aka Sue, the best preserved Tyrannosaurus rex skeleton ever discovered on an archeological dig.

Throughout the ride, you'll see other famous kinds of dinosaurs. A carnotaurus, velociraptor, saltasaurus, a hadrosaur, and a compsognathus are all visible. At one point, a pterodactyl even attacks from above. The carnotaurus is arguably the scariest moment in the ride, and Disney knows this. They take your picture at the precise moment when you come face to face with a 25-feet long monster. On some level, you know that the monster is fake, but nobody will be able to tell from the photograph! The realism of these dinosaurs is amazing, even by Disney's lofty standards.

THE EXPERIENCE

Building a vehicle able to move through the land before time

THE TRICK

Repurposing EMV technology from Indiana Jones Adventure

While the rides have little in common from a theming perspective, DINOSAUR does have sibling of a kind. Indiana Jones Adventure at Disneyland employs the same EMV technology and was actually the first attraction to do so.

At the time, Imagineers evaluated the tricky nature of that attraction's set pieces. Guests needed to move from place to place within the so-called Temple of the Forbidden Eye. The ride couldn't be smooth, though. Guests were supposed to be in peril at all times, and so Disney constructed a ride cart that would deliver a bumpy ride.

As park planners strategized on their new Countdown to Extinction attraction, they understood that the same contrivances were needed. The premise of the ride is that a person travels back in time to the moment when meteors plummet from the sky, causing an extinction-level event. Guests aren't supposed to stare up at the comet strike, though. The dinosaurs were always the focus, even before that was the name of the attraction.

To keep guests looking in the right places, the spots where they'd spent so much money crafting AA dinosaurs, they needed to control the line of sight. And they had just created a vehicle that did it perfectly. So, Imagineers repurposed the Enhanced Motion Vehicle (EMV) to make it a "time machine." They even gave it a cheeky name, the CTX Time Rover. What does the CTX part stand for? Countdown to Extinction, of course! The DINOSAUR version of the EMV is absolutely identical under the hood. The only change is the style, which is time machine-themed.

Despite the brilliant technology of the EMV, Imagineers don't want you thinking about it during the ride. Instead, the focus is always on the prehistoric creatures. One of the ways they distract you is with fog. It's an insidious form of manipulation. When you have trouble seeing something you look that much harder.

DINOSAUR features one of the largest fog machines that Disney (or anybody else) has ever built, and it's there to add a sense of mystery to the proceedings. Without it, you wouldn't buy into the illusion as much. You'd think too much about your ride rather than the dinosaurs. These little touches are what elevate the DINOSAUR experience. It's one of the most immersive attractions at Walt Disney World due to its tight theming.

CHAPTER SEVENTEEN

BUZZ LIGHTYEAR'S SPACE RANGER SPIN

When you and your friends are feeling competitive at Magic Kingdom or Disneyland, you know where to go! Since 1998, Magic Kingdom has delivered tons of fun for friends who want to wage war on the intergalactic battlefield, and Disneyland later joined Star Command in its fight against a malevolent emperor. This videogame deftly disguised as an attraction is different each time you play it, and the underlying Imagineering concepts are sublime. Let's go behind the ride to learn all the secrets of Buzz Lightyear's Space Ranger Spin aka Buzz Lightyear's Astro Blasters.

THE EXPERIENCE

Bringing Buzz Lightyear's fever dreams to life

THE TRICK

Creating an intergalactic, fully immersive environment

You may feel a bit jaded about the several Buzz Lightyear rides around the world. You've ridden them so many times by now that you take for granted the majestic backdrop of the attraction. What you've forgotten is how remarkable a feat Buzz Lightyear was during its early days.

Toy Story the movie came out in 1995. At the time, Pixar was an upstart computer animation company that Disney wouldn't purchase for another decade. Building a Walt Disney World attraction based on a Pixar film was a daring decision at the time. The only other major non-Disney licenses at Walt Disney World at the time were *Star Wars* and *The Twilight Zone*. Also, Pixar was the competition. They were trying to horn in on the animated film industry, Disney's bread and butter for 60 years and counting!

Fortunately, park planners weren't territorial about animated cinema. To the contrary, they delighted in the adventures of Woody and Buzz and wanted to bring them to life in an attraction. Woody's time would have to wait until Toy Story: Midway Mania!. Buzz got the call first. His backstory naturally lent itself to a theme park ride.

Toy Story buffs know that Buzz is a manufactured toy, but he believes that he's a member of Star Command. These soldiers are, for lack of better terminology, guardians of the galaxy. Their primary mission is to defeat Zurg, the nefarious ruler of a planet named Z (somehow spelled Xrghthung).

The Buzz Lightyear attraction brings the plight of Star Command to light. You must battle a swarm of evil robots, all of which are programmed to enforce Zurg's will. But the conceit of this ride is that the robots are only an aggravation.

Your real mission is to prevent Zurg from claiming batteries to fuel his killbot armada. So, you'll see bad guys throughout the ride, but you'll mainly aim at the batteries of Little Green Aliens. Their ships need these batteries to travel through space, but they also double as power supplies for Zurg's killer droids.

The construct of Buzz Lightyear Space Ranger Spin and its siblings is that you are new to Star Command. You must prove yourself by claiming as many batteries as possible. Armed with a starship and your special gun, you head out into the blackness of space, where you will encounter Zurg at one point. It's world-building done right, which explains why the ride is so timeless in nature.

THE EXPERIENCE

A Star Command vessel with full movement

THE TRICK

Modifying a classic Disney vehicle to modernize it

The immersive nature of Space Ranger Spin is critical to its popularity. To provide this escapism, Imagineers had to construct a ride cart that felt at home in outer space. It also needed to operate at reliable speeds to assure appropriate throughput, a pragmatic consideration for park planners. To achieve both goals, Disney returned to one of its classic inventions.

The Buzz Lightyear ride employs third generation Omnimover technology. The carts are all interconnected on the same structures, and they move at a controlled pace. This solves the throughput concern. Disney added a new trick for this particular vehicle, though.

Your starship is capable of 360-degree movement! Outer space is 3-D, and so Imagineers decided that Star Command trainees would require full range of motion. On a practical level, this design puts the Spin in Space Ranger Spin. Should you miss a battery, you have the ability to turn all the way around to keep shooting at it.

When you're in the midst of battle, you might take this movement for granted, but it's revolutionary for an Omnimover. For the first time, Disney stopped controlling the line of sight of Omnimover vehicles. Instead, they ceded full control to theme park tourists, a huge step in the advancement of ride design. It's in stark contrast to an Omnimover design like the Doom Buggy, which narrows your focus to a specific part of the Haunted Mansion attraction. Space Ranger Spin is a liberated interpretation of the original Omnimover concept.

THE EXPERIENCE

Shooting your way to bragging rights

THE TRICK

Laser tag concepts converted for a Disney attraction

While the backdrop and ride system of Space Ranger Spin are fascinating, what people care about the most is the game itself. It's what makes every ride experience different. It's also what keeps bringing people back. No matter who you are or who you're with, you'll feel competitive the moment that you join Star Command. When you have those batteries in your sights, you'll want to prove your skill by attaining massive totals and thereby gaining the associated bragging rights.

How does the gaming system work? Disney took a simple concept that was already in the zeitgeist at the time and plussed it. At the core, the Buzz Lightyear attraction is a glorified game of laser tag! The simple but elegant point-and-click system from that popular game is on full display here, only with special Disney touches.

Each ride cart comes equipped with two laser pistols and a joystick. On the Magic Kingdom version of the attraction, the pistols remain in place. The Disneyland iteration advanced the concept so that guests can move the guns and thereby fire more accurately. Score this round for the Happiest Place on Earth.

The purpose of the laser pistols is to aim at bullseyes, hard targets shown on each battery. You'll know them by the accompanying Z for Zurg. The signal from the laser pistol notifies the system when your aim is true. When you "hit" a Z, you score points, just as a laser tag player's armor lights up to signify a hit.

The joystick's presence emphasizes the genius of the ride cart. You use it to "control" the vehicle, turning it in the direction of your preferred target. At least, that's the intent. In practice, most people work the joystick to guarantee that their friends miss their shots...and also get annoyed. The joystick's presence is what gives the ride the full 360-degree range of motion. While it's true that Space Ranger Spin is a kindred spirit to laser tag, it's the superior version due to these Disney touches.

THE EXPERIENCE

Scoring the most points and thereby claiming victory

THE TRICK

Well...

Okay, this section isn't your standard *Behind the Ride* secrets reveal. Instead, it's a compilation of a few helpful tips so that you can master the Buzz Lightyear scoring system.

The first tip is to trust the controller. This attraction is different from Midway Mania. In that game, you must perform an action to fire. With Buzz Lightyear, you can just hold down the trigger. It will auto-fire. Since accuracy isn't a scoring mechanism on this ride, never let go of the trigger. You may get lucky with some stray shots that hit targets, even when you're not aiming!

You'll also want to locate the high value targets in each section of the ride. The most famous of these is Zurg himself. In the darkened area where Zurg's spaceship is off in the distance, aim for the lowest target onscreen, which is actually beneath Zurg. It's worth many more points than Zurg is.

Similarly, the start of the ride is home to a Rock 'Em Sock 'Em-looking robot that is orangish-red in color. It moves its hands up and down. You want to hit the target on the left robo-paw. Then, find the volcano in the main area. Aim for all the targets on it to score hundreds of thousands of points in quick succession! You can really spike your point totals once you know where to aim.

Finally, you can turn a negative into a positive. Omnimover attractions are notorious for stopping at inopportune times. On other rides, that's a problem. On Buzz Lightyear, it's a chance to score lots of points when the clock's not moving. Yes, as long as you're on the ride, you can add to your point total, even if it's not moving! Anytime there's a pause, use this opportunity to spin around and hit every target in sight.

Presuming that you've followed all of these tips, you'll unlock a special achievement. A score of 999,999 aka Galactic Hero comes with a hidden benefit, an Easter egg of sorts. Take a picture of your total and show it to a cast member. They'll give you a special sticker that proves you're a master of the Buzz Lightyear ride.

CHAPTER EIGHTEEN

ROCK 'N' ROLLER COASTER STARRING AEROSMITH

Though Walt Disney World has never been known for crafting white-knuckle attractions, in the late 1990s, the vaunted Imagineering team pitched an idea for a kickass version of an existing premise: a modern take on the indoor steel roller coaster. This proposed ride would hurtle guests at breakneck speeds, all while leaving them in the dark about what was right in front of them and providing some awesome music at the same time. Of course, you now know this attraction as Rock 'n' Roller Coaster Starring Aerosmith. Let's go behind the ride to discover how it works.

THE EXPERIENCE

Hanging out with Aerosmith in the recording studio

THE TRICK

Filming an introductory video with the band

The design of Rock 'n' Roller Coaster requires a bit of creative license. People who enter the facility learn that they are hanging out at Aerosmith's recording studio. In a few moments, the band will dash around town in order to reach their destination, a live performance. Disney's Imagineers deserve a lot of credit for this tactic, because it accomplishes several tasks at first.

Primarily, the waiting area with the interactions with the band serves a purpose as an effective line queue system. Once people standing in line reach the indoor portion of the attraction, they realize they are only minutes away from enjoying the ride. Plus, the inside part has two main areas, one of which is still part of the line. The other is the meet and greet with

Aerosmith via a looped video. Both parts provide air-conditioning on humid days as well as heating during those rare moments on the Florida calendar when it's chilly.

By providing the Aerosmith video, Imagineers bisect the line queue into the pre-show and post-show areas. This tactic offers the ancillary benefit of providing more accurate line estimations. More importantly, it also controls the filter of people into the indoor waiting area beside the actual ride carts.

To make the sequence seem more realistic, the video shows all the members of Aerosmith recording at G-Force Studios. Their manager informs them that they're late for the show, and the two leaders of the band, Joe Perry and Steven Tyler, decide that they must show some common courtesy to the fans standing in line to watch them record. So, Steven Tyler offers everyone a limo ride to the show.

The instant people exit the video room, they start to stand in a second line that is only a few minutes away from the roller coaster ride. It's a tight combination of atmospheric music production, storytelling, and an introduction to the band for those few people who are unfamiliar with Aerosmith.

THE EXPERIENCE

Massive acceleration in the blink of an eye

THE TRICK

Disney rejoins the roller coaster arms race

Rock 'n' Roller Coaster afforded Imagineers a rare opportunity to let go. They could build a coaster worthy of the Disney name, and since it was going to be integrated with the music of Aerosmith, they had creative license to make certain it rocked. Disney has historically shunned the constant escalation of roller coasters since its beginning in the late 1980s, but Imagineers relished the idea of building the world's fastest limo ride.

Designers already had a solid blueprint for how to proceed thanks to the iconic Space Mountain. All they had to do was modernize those principles while adding a heavy dose of adrenaline. They correctly decided to start with a bang. Rock 'n' Roller Coaster employs a singularly unique component for a Disney attraction: It goes from a dead stop to its maximum speed of 57mph in 2.8 seconds.

To put that into perspective, consider that Tesla received a tremendous amount of press for their addition of Ludicrous Mode. Its acceleration is almost identical to the one Disney managed in 1999. And here's a pro tip for Rock 'n' Roller Coaster regarding that ridiculous, immediate acceleration. The safety guide says to place your head against the back of seat. You'll want to do that. Otherwise, you'll be banging your head often enough early in the ride that you may wind up in the concussion protocol.

Seriously, this ride isn't for people with queasy stomachs. The first inversion delivers a 4.5G wallop, which surpasses what an astronaut feels during a Space Shuttle launch! The core concept is that Rock 'n' Roller Coaster simulates Los Angeles traffic, so the inversions are freeway loops. You hurtle through the streets like Vin Diesel after a nitrous oxide boost, and it is pitch black. You have no idea what's coming next. The street signs whip by at a breakneck pace, leaving you but one lingering thought: this limo driver will not be getting a big tip.

THE EXPERIENCE

The most reckless limousine ride ever

THE TRICK

Maximizing throughput with a roller coaster

In order to accomplish the grand design for the roller coaster, the limo has to be perfect. There are two phases to the design. The first is providing enough traffic to mitigate the anticipated giant lines for an actual Walt Disney World roller coaster. They accomplished this by emphasizing the limo concept. Automobile manufacturers build these vehicles to host dozens of passengers.

By following this precept, Imagineers had a viable explanation for deploying a limo cart capable of holding 24 people. The ride has a tremendous guest throughput for a roller coaster, particularly given the 82-second length of the entire experience. The Aerosmith introductory video lasts quite a bit longer than the actual roller coaster portion. The thrill-in-a-minute experience is so extraordinary, however, that most guests never notice the brief duration. Many of them couldn't handle a substantially longer dark ride with that much G-force in play, anyway.

THE EXPERIENCE

Rocking out to Aerosmith classics

THE TRICK

Randomizing Aerosmith songs as background soundtrack

One big reason why the ride works so beautifully is its sound integration. Disney targeted Aerosmith for a specific reason. They're in many ways the Great American Band, and they have numerous hits that mesh majestically with a thrill ride. Imagineers highlight this union throughout the attraction.

There are more than 900 speakers sprinkled through the interior and exterior. The limo itself offers five of them. Two are positioned by the ears while two more are at the shoulders. A subwoofer lies beneath your feet. If you don't like rock music or Aerosmith in particular, this is not the ride for you. There is no escaping their sound throughout Rock 'n' Roller Coaster.

In fact, Joe Perry and Steven Tyler actually re-recorded some of their music in order to accentuate high points of the songs in union with seminal moments in the ride. There is also variability in the songs you'll hear. The individual limos all contain their own song, songs, or medley. Only two of them, "Sweet Emotion" and "Nine Lives," are played without interruption.

There are a total of six other songs you could potentially hear on the ride, one of which is available in two different limos. Disney chose the ones that they felt blended the best with the ride. There is a pair of two-song medleys. One of them features "Love in an Elevator" and "Walk This Way," and the other includes snippets from "Back in the Saddle" and "Dude Looks Like a Lady." Another limo includes a triple medley of "F.I.N.E.," "Young Lust," and "Love in an Elevator." The two standalone songs are a live version of "Sweet Emotion" and the studio version of "Nine Lives." If you have a favorite of these, read the section below to learn how you can game the system.

THE EXPERIENCE

Theming the background details perfectly

THE TRICK

Putting Aerosmith into every ride aspect

The band attended the opening of the ride on July 29, 1999. Joe Perry and Steven Tyler rode the ride together a dozen times during a sneak preview. They also provided suggestions on the layout of the recording studio. Given their infamous *60 Minutes* interview, it may have been the last time all of them got along.

The stretch limo is modeled after an early 1960s Cadillac. Disney doesn't say which one, but most people believe it's the 1962 edition.

Given the space limitations Disney faces in adding new attractions to popular areas of the parks, they had to be creative. This coaster sits in an area that was once a cast member parking lot.

It was the first ride at Walt Disney World to feature multiple inversions. It's got two loops and a corkscrew.

The Imagineers love to leave their mark on their creations. If you listen carefully to the intercom at G-Force Records, you'll hear names called. They're the name of various Disney Imagineers who worked to create the roller coaster.

The only attraction at Disney World with a faster top speed than Rock 'n' Roller Coaster is Test Track, which reaches 64.9 mph.

Three years after its debut at Hollywood Studios, Disney duplicated Rock 'n' Roller Coaster almost exactly at Disneyland Paris. It's the fastest attraction there.

The giant guitar that's a signature part of the exterior is four stories tall. It's approximately 40 feet in stature, although it's hard to tell since it rests at an angle.

There are two famous people who work at G-Force Records. One of them is Illeana Douglas, one of the hardest working actresses in Hollywood. She is best known for *Six Feet Under*, *Entourage*, *Seinfeld*, and *Action*. The other is Ken Marino, an original member of MTV's *The State*. He is a featured player in *Party Down*, *Burning Love*, and *Childrens Hospital*. Most people know him from his work on *Veronica Mars*, though.

While the ride features five different limos, only four of them ever operate at once. Each of them has a silly license plate for you to suss out the meaning:

- 2FAST4U
- UGOBABE (formerly UGOGIRL)

- BUHBYE
- 1QKLIMO
- H8TRFFC

The license plate identifies which soundtrack you'll hear during the ride. 2FAST4U offers a live version of Sweet Emotion. UGOBABE provides a "Love in an Elevator"/"Walk This Way" mash-up. BUHBYE is the three-song medley. H8TRFFC has the "Back in the Saddle"/"Dude Looks Like a Lady" combo. And 1QKLIMO plays "Nine Lives."

CHAPTER NINETEEN

TEST TRACK

Test Track has been a staple of Walt Disney World's Epcot since its debut in 1998. As the fastest ride at the park, it has the reputation of being one of the few true thrill rides across the four Disney theme parks in Orlando. Several years ago, it underwent refurbishments that augmented Test Track's style. Gone is the yellow/black checkerboard design that caused riders to feel like crash test dummies. In its stead are slick, Tron-inspired blue colors that dazzle with their brilliance. The new version of Test Track is a technological marvel that meshes style and substance in a single glorious ride experience. Let's go behind the ride to determine how the new and improved Test Track looks under the hood.

THE EXPERIENCE

The Tron Ride

THE TRICK

A video-game feel for an aging ride

Test Track assistant project manager Melissa Jeselnick:

> But as the vehicle industry evolved, we decided to go back and explore a new story that reflects these evolutions. As a result, this iteration of Test Track celebrates vehicle design and an optimistic view of the future.

General Motors had been the sponsor of Test Track since its debut. In fact, if you loved the previous World of Motion, you should blame them, because their fingerprints are all over the murder weapon that killed that attraction. They wanted to sponsor a thrill ride instead. After the longest delay in the history of Walt Disney World, Test Track launched in 1998.

Once Disney decided to renovate the previous iteration of Test Track, GM determined that only one of their brands should become the focus of the new version. The Chevrolet Design Center was revealed in 2012, and the breathtaking additions immediately created shockwaves among long time Disney fans. The Test Track that they knew had been traded in for a younger, hotter model. Interior color schemes accentuate the splashy blue world created in *Tron* by placing them against black backdrops. It's the kind of neon paradise ordinarily reserved for Las Vegas. The entire interior area is illuminated to craft the illusion that a person has entered the world of Tron.

To that end, the visual majesty of *Tron* is reflected throughout the attraction experience. In the movie, a programmer is transported into the realm created by his code. The premise of Test Track is that once you build a vehicle, you are transported to a test track where you test its ability. Amusingly, *Tron* isn't the only Disney movie to which Test Track pays tribute via its visuals, though. The sign "Turn Right to Go Left" is an actual quote from *Cars*.

THE EXPERIENCE

Design your dream car

THE TRICK

Design your Frankenstein car may be a better description

For people who wait in line for Test Track, the first part of the ride experience occurs prior to the ride cart. Utilizing technological advances in RFID technology, Disney Imagineers have crafted a pre-ride car simulator. A person's RFID card (or magic band) is employed as an identifier, and a competition unfolds wherein everyone tries to build the most capable vehicle.

A series of touch screens provide options about the style of car, starting with size and eventually evolving into more technical details. The user has the ability to define the length and width then sculpt to craft the style that best suits them. Some engine choices are also enabled. Menu options include solar drive, fuel cell, EV hybrid, gas engine, super charged, plasma burner, and eco electricity. Further customization is available, depending on the current wait time for Test Track.

After all choices have been selected, a person is provided with a visual of their "dream car," although it looks like The Homer more often than not. The last time I tried it, my car wound up looking like The Batmobile after a 20-car pile-up.

Since some people *do* have skill as car designers, Test Track allows people to compete to see whose vehicle is most functional. Designs are tested in the categories of capability, efficiency, responsiveness, and power, with a maximum of 100 in each category. The fuller your circle is, the stronger your prototype will perform in this evaluation. Most people clean up in the power department while their efficiency score would lead to about three miles a gallon on the road.

After people finish their designs, there are a couple of other tricks to be done via RFID. The post-ride area interacts with the cards to reveal the overall grades for the designs. If you want a point of comparison, I scored a 206 with my vehicular monstrosity. Some Elon Musk wannabe put my results to shame with their 227. The worst part is that I was already married to the little prima donna.

THE EXPERIENCE

A Test Track experience

THE TRICK

The sim track tests your design

While pre-ride activities comprise between five and nine minutes of interactive entertainment, the ride is still the thing at Epcot. Test Track would not have the reputation of one of the best overall rides at Walt Disney World without a thrilling ride experience. Its attention to detail in re-creating a crash test simulation is what differentiates Test Track as a masterful ride.

Car designs are tested by navigating a course of massive acceleration, hairpin turns, and sharp stops. The user swipes their smart card to identify and upload their precise prototype to employ during the evaluation phase. After entering the car, the rider is dropped into the *Tron*-styled world. The Sim Track connects with OnStar in a second shameless bit of consumerism on top of the existing Chevrolet tie-in. Then, a weather event that looks like a cross between a comet strike and a car Derezzing occurs. This signifies the beginning of the four tests, where you are almost struck by lightning and hit by a futuristic 18-wheeler in a matter of about 10 seconds. Frankly, if you have that kind of luck as a driver, you should probably stay off the road.

Of course, the previous work is less important than the adrenaline rush that occurs once the rider exits the indoor portion of Test Track. The first hint of sunshine establishes that the true velocity is about to occur. What transpires afterward is many people's favorite part of Epcot. The car explodes into daylight at a maximum velocity of 64.9 miles per hour. The disconnect between the Tron visuals indoors and the brilliant Florida sunshine is startling at first. Once your eyes adjust, the pure speed rush is all that matters.

If there is any complaint about Test Track, it's that once you reach the open air outside, the simulation part of the ride takes a backseat to the adrenaline spike. Then again, that sensation may be intentional. The instant the car follows the track back inside, the scoreboard above identifies the placement of the participating riders. Winning first place is a moment that will satisfy all of the racecar driver wannabes in the world.

THE EXPERIENCE

A ride to remember

THE TRICK

RFID technology captures everything

After you exit your test car, the Test Track experience is not complete. The post-race area includes a Chevrolet showcase that presents several tremendous opportunities for pictures. You can insert yourself into several settings, many of which involve Chevrolet products. There is also the area where your scores are publicized, making you a hero or goat among your Test Track peers. The beauty of RFID technology is that everything you've done up to this point has been leading to your final Test Track grade. You can use your smart card to integrate your car and yourself into various other Chevrolet Showroom games. Plus, you have the opportunity to take a picture of your imaginary vehicle to show off to your friends.

CHAPTER TWENTY

EXPEDITION EVEREST

In 1998, Disney debuted their first newly created park in almost a decade. Expectations were sky high, and most people realize that the initial reactions were decidedly mixed. After garnering 8.6 million visits in 1998, park attendance steadily declined to 7.3 million in 2002, a number it matched in 2003.

On the fifth anniversary of the park's debut, Disney wanted to make a splash. They announced construction for a revolutionary new ride. It would not only compete with some of the headline grabbing, adrenaline-spiking roller coasters being built at other theme parks but also deliver a signature view in the sprawling Animal Kingdom landscape.

Expedition Everest was the ride, and no expense would be spared to make it the ultimate park experience. $100 million was ultimately invested in its creation, making it almost as expensive as the movie Cars, the first Pixar release after Disney acquired that company in 2006. $100 million was such an unprecedented financial outlay for a theme park ride that it was still listed in the Guinness Book of World Records as the most expensive roller coaster in the world a full five years later.

Disney got their money's worth. Expedition Everest remains one of the signature attractions at Animal Kingdom. It is one of the most thematic ride park experiences in the world, featuring breathtaking visuals and G-force of 2.7 that happens in the dark. And let's not forget the 22-foot-tall state-of-the-art animatronic Yeti. Expedition Everest is a hallmark achievement in engineering. Read on to discover how it works.

THE EXPERIENCE

Re-creating Nepal

THE TRICK

Importing thousands of Nepalese knick-knacks

The Nepalese town of Serka Zong in the fictional kingdom of Anandapur is the location, and Disney spared no expense in creating the most realistic fictional city imaginable. Imagineers trekked to the Himalayas in order to understand the indigenous culture. Some of the pictures taken during expeditions are displayed in the museum/wait line for the ride.

With a nine-figure budget, there is obviously a lot of attention to detail utilized to create the atmospheric Royal Anandapur Tea Company and accompanying Yeti Museum. Over 8,000 genuine Nepalese items were purchased to be integrated into the ride area. If you have ever noted the astounding authenticity of the props on display, this is the explanation. They are the real deal rather than re-creations.

THE EXPERIENCE

An arduous adventure through the Forbidden Mountain

THE TRICK

Making the mountain

Building a man-made mountain is an arduous task rather than an easy one, despite what you may believe because of Disney. After all, the theme park masters have built about 20 of them over the years starting with The Matterhorn Bobsleds in 1959.

In order to differentiate it from the rest, the mountain setting for Expedition Everest had to be eye-grabbing in an original way. Rather than compete with the new style of giga-roller coasters popping up across the world, Disney's Imagineers chose to focus upon what they do best: atmosphere.

Using a forced perspective, Everest is re-created as a background peak off in the distance to the right, thereby creating the sensation that the dazzling landmark in question, the Forbidden Mountain, is much larger than the 200 feet tall.

Disney's vaunted attention to detail and expertise in line of sight causes the short mountain to dominate the landscape across Animal Kingdom without requiring massive height for the actual structure. Simply by crafting a mountain range rather than a sole mountain, the Yeti's residence looks gigantic. It is a blueprint example of how to make less seem like more.

THE EXPERIENCE

Riding backwards into the mountain

THE TRICK

A brilliant visual and a surprising twist

The premise of the ride is that the visitor is journeying from one destination in the Himalayas to another. In order to navigate the vast distance quickly, people on the expedition ride a passenger train to Everest. There is only one problem. The train involves a shortcut through the Forbidden Mountain area protected by a territorial Yeti. And the Yeti wants to wreck the infringing vehicle.

In order to escape the monster, the rider is redirected onto a different set of tracks, narrowly avoiding disaster. By defying expectations and thrusting the user backward, an element of surprise is created off the bat. How many roller coasters in the world guide you along the path to broken tracks, only to divert you backward at extreme velocity?

Amazingly, all that is required to pull off such a memorable feat is a second set of tracks. As the user is propelled upward to the broken section, they ride on a visible portion of tracks. Once the visual danger is revealed, the carts are pulled back onto a track segment that cannot be seen from the frontal view the rider has. And even if they could see it, they would be distracted by the broken tracks ahead. In this manner, Disney employs the same misdirection magicians use in their craft.

THE EXPERIENCE

Coming face-to-face with a giant Yeti

THE TRICK

Building a ground-shaking Audio-Animatronic

Even though a rider spends only a brief moment in plain view of the Yeti, Disney's vaunted ride builders wanted the experience to be as realistic as possible. As *Popular Mechanics* notes about the construction, "the beast became an object of obsessive perfectionism from Disney's Imagineers."

To enhance the realism, vertical as well as horizontal slides were employed in order to maximize the movement potential of the beast. It had a range of two feet of vertical motion plus five feet of horizontal motion. So, if it were real, its movement ability would be deadly.

A whopping 6,000 pounds of fur was used to create the memorable look of the killer Yeti. Imagine if your dress garments required 250 zippers and 1,000 snaps in order to suit up each day. That is the type of attention to detail that distinguishes Disney. The ensemble dramatically increases the overall weight of the animatronic, estimated at 20,000 pounds.

The Yeti is so heavy that the creature is airborne. No legs could support such girth. Amusingly, its legs and left arm are unpowered. Their movement occurs naturally, like a puppet, as the regular motions of the other ligaments propel them.

Not content with the visual alone, a 3,000 psi hydraulic thruster was implemented to power the animatronic. Engineers claimed that the Yeti has more power than a 747 jet engine. And all it tries to do is smack you. Imagine the force if it ever did.

Unfortunately, many guests will be aware that the Yeti animatronic has not functioned as intended for years. A few months after the ride opened, the foundation on which the Yeti stands was damaged, and his full range of movements was put to an end. Instead, a strobe light now flashes behind him to give the impression that he is moving—earning the creature the nickname "Disco Yeti."

CHAPTER TWENTY-ONE

TOY STORY MANIA!

THE EXPERIENCE

A carnival game starring your favorite *Toy Story* characters

THE TRICK

Disney buys Pixar

By the end of the 20th century, Pixar Studios had established itself as the premiere animation company in the world, briefly usurping a title long held by the Walt Disney Company.

In 1995, Pixar's *Toy Story* became the number one North American release of the year. In 1999, *Toy Story 2* faced some slightly stiffer competition in the form of *Star Wars: Episode One—The Phantom Menace*. Still, the second adventure of Woody and Buzz grossed 35% more than its predecessor on the way to becoming the third best global release of the year.

Over the next several years, Pixar asserted its dominance with a string of masterpieces such as *Monsters, Inc.*, *The Incredibles*, and *Finding Nemo*. The genteel nature of *Toy Story* and its subtle but pointed storytelling permeated throughout the later Pixar releases. In January of 2006, after acknowledging they were no longer the masters of the animated release, Disney purchased Pixar and named its leader, John Lasseter, as the company's chief creative officer.

The merging of Pixar and Disney has proven to be a masterstroke due to the evergreen toy revenue of their intellectual property. Not every aspect of the acquisition was about money, though. Disney executives sagely recognized that the bread and butter of the company, its theme parks, could be rejuvenated with the addition of some Pixar flair.

The strategy had already paid dividends prior to the merger. Buzz Lightyear's Space Ranger Spin had been introduced in 1998, and the Omnimover shooter ride proved extremely popular, especially with the youngest visitors at Disney's parks. The odd juxtaposition of a shooting gallery with a dark ride created an atmospheric videogame setting that thrilled the under-10 crowd while providing a relaxing, air-conditioned ride for parents.

Disney knew when they bought Pixar that they would want more rides featuring iconic characters. Still, the crown jewel of the company's intellectual property library has always been a story about a cowboy and a space ranger. If they were going to do a ride designed for *Toy Story* fans, it would have to be a masterpiece. Imagineers quickly went to work on just such a ride.

THE EXPERIENCE

Playing a video game on a theme park ride

THE TRICK

Creating a 4-D ride experience that somehow feels retro

In 2008, Toy Story Mania! debuted at Disney California Adventure and Disney's Hollywood Studios. Over the past several years, it has become one of the signature theme park attractions, as demonstrated by its consistent hour plus wait times at Hollywood Studios (the Hollywood Studios version of the ride is now called Toy Story Mania!). Everything about this self-proclaimed 4-D ride is triumphant, but how does it work?

A key part of the appeal of *Toy Story* is hidden in plain sight in the name. It is a celebration of childhood toys, one that adults love for the bittersweet memories and children love for the immediacy. In strategizing about how to attain the perfect tone for a *Toy Story* experience, Imagineers settled upon a carnival game. After all, the early, amateurish predecessor to the amusement park is the carnival, and the fact that they still exist to this day is a tribute to the warmth of childhood memories made. What is the most memorable part of the carnival experience? It is playing games for prizes, of course!

Disney's designers faced an important question at this juncture. How would someone enjoy the down and dirty carny game experience at a state of the art amusement park? The answer was obviously to re-create that same sensation but in a fresh way. Given the popularity of the Buzz Lightyear game,

Imagineers understandably wanted to mimic some of the videogame mechanics in order to foster a competitive environment. It became the 21st century equivalent of trying to bust three plates to win a stuffed animal.

Toy Story Mania! is a state of the art 4-D videogame ride masquerading as a simplistic shoot 'em up. Thematically and symbolically, it even makes players "reach for the sky." You've probably played it and maybe even bragged to your friends about getting a high score. Even so, there is a lot you probably didn't know. Here are some of the tricks employed by the attraction.

THE EXPERIENCE

Splashy *Toy Story* graphics

THE TRICK

Powerful computers and images...for the first time

As they participate in a series of mini-games, riders view the Toy Story characters and their surroundings in three dimensions. Simply wearing the 3-D glasses is not enough to create a 3-D environment. You are handed those dual-colored shades for a reason. In order to enjoy the effects of the splashy graphics, the behind-the-scenes computer system is overwhelmingly complicated. 154 graphics workstations are seamlessly integrated under a program that runs on—don't laugh—Windows XP.

The system renders 60 images per second, the same amount used for HDTV broadcast. So, every moment of the ride experience is the equivalent of a playing a videogame in HD. While that may not sound as impressive now, it was a mind-boggling accomplishment in 2008. I mean, Windows XP! Your phone probably has a more advanced operating system than that.

THE EXPERIENCE

Swiveling vehicles

THE TRICK

Computer-controlled ride cart motion

As they travel around the circuit, riders' cars swivel to face the screens and other ride elements. This may not sound like a crucial component of the ride—until you watch a YouTube video. When you are playing Toy Story Mania!, you rarely stop to consider how much you are being spun around. Only when you watch video of the experience do you realize how often you get twisted. It's done to add a layer of difficulty to the playing experience. Without the swivels, a straight shooter would clean up.

The vehicles are equipped with programmable logic controllers, which alert the control system wirelessly as to the vehicle's current location and speed. A wired network embedded in the track sends instructions back to the vehicles from the central controller, ensuring that they are always in the right place at the right time.

THE EXPERIENCE

Five different ride "levels"

THE TRICK

Complex network server interactions

Five classic carnival games comprise the Toy Story Mania! experience. Each of them provides a different gameplay mechanic. In order to achieve this, no fewer than four gaming systems are required in each ride cart to maintain constant communication with the overriding network server. The Windows XP infrastructure signals each computer monitor the appropriate information in order to display the appropriate game for the area where the cart is currently positioned. A series of 10" LCD displays are carefully positioned to allow players to track their performance during each round.

THE EXPERIENCE

Firing with a pull-string gun

THE TRICK

Creating a modified, interactive popgun

Riders use a pull-string to control each of the different games, enabling them to "throw' balls, fire darts, and more. Since Toy Story Mania! is not a true video game, Imagineers faced a challenge in how to define the "A" button—the button on the controller that gets mashed repeatedly to make sure that Green Elf does not need food badly. Rather than hand actual controllers to players, an expensive solution that would expose Disney to item damage and theft, Imagineers delivered an inventive solution.

A modified popgun was added for each user. The introduction of this is important, because one of the target demographics for this ride is the under-10 crowd. They expect all phases of a ride to be interactive. The pull-string gun means that even if they do not enjoy aiming at targets, it is still a joyous procedure to pull the string repeatedly. As always, Disney employees are inventive about enhancing every phase of a ride.

The spring-action gun contains sensors that provide information on its orientation to the control system. This is combined with information on the position and orientation of the vehicle to generate the on-screen animation and to decide whether a target has been successfully hit or not.

THE EXPERIENCE

Interactive special effects

THE TRICK

Unprecedented computer gaming controls

Anyone who hits a special target is rewarded in some regard. The interactive nature of the game, the 4-D as it were, is to provide a blast of air, misting of water or memorable smell. The key to accomplishing this trick again exists within the underlying computer system. Siemens Energy & Automation crafted a special control set for automation. At the time of the ride's debut, this series of controls was unprecedented.

In addition to including one PC for each of the 56 game screens, other (Windows XP) PCs are used to control each game's special effects. Two tracking systems inform the control system of the vehicle's precise location (which can slightly—the cars do not park in the same spot every time), ensuring that the accompanying effects can be triggered appropriately.

In order to squirt a player, three things must happen. The computer must display the target, it must recognize that the user has struck the target, and it must immediately disperse a blast of air, moisture or odor. Imagine the precise level of programming required to accomplish that feat.

In fact, that exactitude exists from the moment you step in the cart until the moment you exit. Toy Story Mania! is a landmark achievement in atmospheric ride creation.

CHAPTER TWENTY-TWO

RADIATOR SPRINGS RACERS

When director John Lasseter envisioned the movie *Cars*, he imagined a throwback to the halcyon days of his youth. It was a time when people across the country would all take the same road, U.S. Route 66, to get where they were going. In this simpler time, the destination was less important than the journey, and cars were integral to the traveling experience.

With global box office of $461 million, *Cars* (Pixar's final film prior to their acquisition by Disney) is a blockbuster by any standard. Where the brand differentiates itself, however, is through toy sales. In the period from its release in 2006 until the first quarter of 2013, *Cars* merchandise earned over $10 billion in revenue. If you're a parent of a child during that timeframe, this is not new information to you, either.

Given the popularity of not just the films but especially the toys, bringing the realm of Radiator Springs to the Disney theme parks was inevitable. The arrival of Cars Land at Disney's California Adventure in 2012 represented one of the largest expansions of any Disney theme park to date. The company spent over a billion dollars renovating and adding to their already established facilities.

The signature attraction in Cars Land is Radiator Springs Racers, which carries a sticker shock-inducing price tag of more than $200 million. It's far and away the most expensive ride ever built at Disneyland, and it's in the conversation for costliest ride of all-time. Since the Cars Land expansion, traffic at the park has increased from 6.34 million in 2011 to 9.57 million in 2017. Obviously, Cars Land is striking a chord with a lot of potential guests, and Radiator Springs Racers is a key reason why. Let's go Behind the Ride to discover all the reasons why Radiator Springs Racers is so popular.

THE EXPERIENCE

Re-creating the Backdrop of Radiator Springs

THE TRICK

Pave a Parking Lot, Put Up a Paradise

Mother Nature is especially good at building mountains. She gets millions of years to provide finished products, though. In the case of Disney's California Adventures, Disney rock-work art director Zsolt Hormay and his team had only a couple of years to build the 125-foot tall mountain range named Ornament Valley. This sandstone mesa encompasses the background landscape for the film version of *Cars* and is therefore crucial to the design of Cars Land.

Disney hired a team of specialists from across the globe who met the twin criteria requisite for the project. They had to possess the construction experience needed to operate on such a large-scale design. They also needed the artisanship to remember that style matters just as much at Disney theme parks as substances. So, a slew of master builders with a track record of artistic achievement were brought onboard.

These professionals welded, sculpted, and painted the entire structure, literally bringing a fictional mountain into reality. In the process, they demolished the prior "Timon" parking lot to put up their mountain, thereby inverting the lyrics of that Joni Mitchell song, Big Yellow Taxi. There are 4,000 tons of steel in the structure of Ornament Valley. Meanwhile, Disney employees spent 28,000 man-hours making it life-like and visually breathtaking. Anyone who has ever visited Cars Land knows that they performed the job masterfully. The man-made mountain highlights the stunning visage of Radiator Springs.

THE EXPERIENCE

Re-creating the World of Cars

THE TRICK

Bringing the Characters of Cars to Life

The folksy charm of *Cars* the movie is predicated upon the genteel nature of its characters. Doc Hudson, Sally Carrera, Ramone, Luigi, Guido, Flo, Sarge, Sheriff, and Fillmore all inhabit the city of Radiator Springs. Each one enriches it with their unique personality, whether you enjoy Fillmore's hippy hijinks, Sheriff's disapproval of said hijinks, Luigi and Guido's love of tires, or Doc's constant wisdom. Creating a *Cars* ride that fails to highlight their communal nature is a pointless exercise. And that goes double for Lightning McQueen and Mater, the stars of *Cars*.

Fortunately, Disney Imagineers employ a clever design element to make the rider feel like they're a guest of Radiator Springs. The styling of the attraction is similar to other Disney theme park staples like Pirates of the Caribbean, It's a Small World, and Splash Mountain, wherein the rider actually encounters the denizens of the realm. With Radiator Springs Racers, that means a brief tour of the "downtown" area of the city, which means the only place where anybody hangs out in this sleepy burg.

The cart takes the rider along a linear path, starting outdoors to highlight the mountains but eventually heading indoors. At this point, a visually stimulating world of shiny cars is waiting to greet the visitor. This is subtle but important, as the premise of *Cars* the movie is that Radiator Springs functions as a brief pit stop for travelers on their journey across the country.

While the tone of the town is understated in the film, the theme park attraction version of the city is filled with eye-grabbing neon lights and stunningly detailed set pieces. Guests drive down the main throughway of Radiator Springs before taking a brief detour to receive car service at Luigi's Casa Della Tires. Since there are no people in this world, only anthropomorphic cars, there is no need for Disney's usual brand of human animatronics. Instead, all the characters from the film are re-created in life-like (well, car-like) fashion during the attraction. Everything you see during Radiator Springs Racers is authentic in this regard.

THE EXPERIENCE

Creating an Atmospheric Thrill Ride

THE TRICK

Repurposing Ideas from Test Track

Walt Disney World's Epcot doesn't have a lot of signature rides, but Test Track has remained a favorite since its debut in 1999. Disney Imagineers are huge fans of recycling work, understanding that a premise that works in one park is likely to prove just as popular elsewhere.

Rather than design an entirely new ride experience for Radiator Springs Racers, Imagineers sagely chose to stick with something they knew worked already. Enter Test Track. The design of this ride involves an indoor and outdoor component. Park guests build their own car design and then test its quality during a series of challenges such as efficiency, responsiveness, and power. Spoiler: Nobody ever does well on efficiency, but everyone aces the power test. After a few near misses indoors, the attraction cart explodes into the outdoor setting and accelerates to 64.9 miles per hour. Those few thrilling moments in the sunlight are a visceral thrill.

Radiator Springs Racers extends the concept a bit. Since the premise of the town is that guests stop by on the way to other places, you actually begin your journey outside. It's a slow sojourn through the beautiful country just beyond the town, including the memorable waterfall from the film. Then, the setting changes to an indoor section. Here's where the unmistakable comparisons to Test Track begin.

Whereas you avoid a random semi-tractor at Epcot, Cars Land thrusts you into the oncoming traffic that is Mack the tractor-trailer. Seconds later, the weather test is replaced by a narrow escape at railroad tracks, a lecture from Sheriff, and an encounter with Mater and some easily spooked tractors. The style and setting are unmistakably similar. The difference is that Test Track employs random situations whereas Radiator Springs Racers maximizes its rider enjoyment via character licensing. It feels like a much more authentic Disney ride in this regard.

THE EXPERIENCE

Racing Like Lightning McQueen

THE TRICK

An Open-Air Adrenaline Rush

After you've enjoyed a tune-up at Luigi's Casa Della Tires or a paint job at Ramone's House of Body Art, Radiator Springs Racers follows the same trajectory as Test Track once again. It thrusts the rider outside, but there is one slight variance. You see a different ride cart to your side, which is the Racers part of the ride title.

The two cars simultaneously explode into the open terrain just outside Radiator Springs, engaging in a competitive race to the finish line. While the start of the attraction is a slow ride through beautiful country, the departure from town is all about pure speed and adrenaline. Of course, since Cars Land is a child-friendly attraction, the maximum velocity is much lower at 40 MPH than the top speed at Test Track.

There is an additional difference, as the fast portion of Radiator Springs Racers is not quite the end of the ride. Instead, the vehicles enter a final dark area where Lightning McQueen and Mater congratulate you on a quality race, naming everyone winners today. He's technically wrong, though. One cart does win each race. Of course, you have no control over whether you emerge victorious or not. One of the two vehicles is randomly selected to add a level of intrigue to each ride.

CHAPTER TWENTY-THREE

SEVEN DWARFS MINE TRAIN

New rides don't come along very often at Magic Kingdom. The reality is that the Walt Disney Company always faces long odds in introducing new elements into their most popular theme park. Guests share a certain expectation about where everything should go and which attractions should always exist. Amusingly, many of the same people also want to enjoy new and exciting experiences while visiting Walt Disney World.

Historically, Disney has combatted these conflicting consumer demands by adding new rides at the other theme parks while constantly renovating the most popular attractions at Magic Kingdom. Sure, there's the occasional repurposing of a space to turn The ExtraTERRORestrial Alien Encounter into Stitch's Great Escape!, but the general practice is to perfect rather than create anew. That's why the introduction of Seven Dwarfs Mine Trains proved so shrewd for the corporation.

While performing an expansion of Fantasyland, Disney opened enough space to add a new roller coaster. The instant crowd pleaser isn't a thrill ride along the lines of Rock 'n' Roller Coaster or Test Track. What it does deliver, however, is a joyous experience starting the moment people enter the line that continues all the way until the final stop of the coaster cart. In fact, the Imagineers saved a special surprise for people when they reach the end of the line. Let's go behind the ride to learn about how Disney developed such a wonderful new attraction.

THE EXPERIENCE

A new roller coaster in an area planned for princesses

THE TRICK

New construction and the discarding of a potential attraction

Okay, this isn't a trick per se, but to appreciate what the Walt Disney Company achieved with Seven Dwarfs Mine Train, you first must understand what they faced. The opportunity to build a new attraction in an established park hub doesn't come around very often for any Disney theme park gate, much less Magic Kingdom, its crown jewel. Building a new attraction in Fantasyland wasn't just about constructing the latest and greatest technological marvel. It was about maintaining the delicate balance of guest satisfaction. Deciphering the perfect balance required a nuanced approach.

As originally intended, Fantasyland would stand as a Disney Princess haven. In 2009, Disney announced their plans for the Fantasyland expansion. The initial blueprints suggested a pair of Princess attractions featuring Ariel and a princess to be named later as the stars. The former became The Little Mermaid: Ariel's Undersea Adventure. The latter...became something different. The Fantasyland expansion was to include a large Pixie Hollow section, a broadening of the same premise that remains at Disneyland today. Disney had opened this Magic Kingdom park setting at Mickey's Toontown Fair in 2008, and they felt satisfied enough with the results to delve deeper into the setting.

Over time, the park planners responsible for New Fantasyland accepted the obvious. The scales of this section tilted undeniably female. I don't see anything wrong with this, as more than half the population is female. If you're going to tip the scales a particular way, targeting women makes more sense than men, statistically speaking. Imagineers felt differently. They wanted everyone to experience the same euphoria once the improved park section opened to the public. So, they dropped Pixie Hollow altogether and reconsidered how to approach the second princess. In the end, they prioritized a family-friendly ride that would appeal to everyone. By the start of 2011, plans were in place for a new roller coaster, albeit one that wouldn't break any land-speed records. After all, that wasn't the point. This new ride would appeal to Disney loyalists who loved a certain fairytale already popular in Fantasyland.

THE EXPERIENCE

Relief from the boredom of waiting in line

THE TRICK

Employing technology in extremely clever ways

Disney enjoys an enviable problem at their theme parks, especially at Walt Disney World. They receive a high volume of traffic from tourists across the globe. That's why half of the most visited theme parks on the planet are Disney's Orlando gates. The downside of this is that the company faces an ongoing struggle to eliminate theme park queues. There's no ultimate solution to this problem. It will always exist in some form.

Rather than sit idly by while customers suffer through agonizingly slow, boring lines, however, Imagineers have aggressively attacked the problem. Seven Dwarfs Mine Train stands as one of their greatest achievements to date in this regard. Imagineers have meticulously timed distractions along the ride queue in order to reduce the amount of aggravation that park visitors endure.

Once people enter the covered part of the line, they start to notice a Bejeweled type of touchscreen videogame. There are multiple consoles available to play, and guests can interact from both sides of the display, meaning that they can play for several minutes if so inclined. Best of all, the interactive game allows multiple participants at once, so there's no fear of someone hogging the game.

This collaborative type of activity spills over into the indoor area. Once people reach the interior part of the queue, they see barrels that they can spin, which is a pitch perfect addition to a dwarf mine attraction. Once people begin to spin, the genius of the apparatus reveals itself on the ceiling. The various dwarfs appear on the roof when people gyrate the barrels quickly enough. If enough people do so at once, a hidden Easter egg unfolds. Snow White herself joins her beloved dwarfs in dancing on the ceiling. Due to its newness and instant popularity, Seven Dwarfs Mine Train claims one of the longest waits at Walt Disney World, frequently in excess of 100 minutes. The enjoyable line games cause a lot of this time to fly by, though.

THE EXPERIENCE

A pleasantly bumpy ride on a twisting coaster

THE TRICK

An inventive new kind of coaster design

One of the many skills that differentiate Imagineers from other ride designers is their ability to think creatively. The people tasked with what would become Seven Dwarfs Mine Train knew from the beginning that this coaster would not go fast. It was replacing Snow White's Scary Adventures, and the focus was on crafting something that the entire family would enjoy. Expedition Everest and Tower of Terror might not be for every Disney tourist, but the Seven Dwarfs ride should satisfy the young and young at heart.

Still, the one thing Disney cast members won't accept is duplication. They demand more of themselves, and that's why Seven Dwarfs Mine Train features a new coaster experience. Each cart twists and turns independently. Imagineers describe it as a "tilting vehicle" design, but they didn't embark on this strategy randomly. Always emphasizing story in all phases, Disney employees recognized that transporting guests on a mine train wouldn't deliver a smooth ride. Instead, they'd suffer through all the bumps of underground train tracks.

Transitioning that concept to an outdoor roller coaster required innovation. Imagineers discovered that they could anchor all the cars in a full mine cart together while still providing individual movement. Think of it like an airplane. Imagine if each row of seats were capable of independent motion. The plane itself goes the correct direction, but the sections can sway back and forth to add a rocking sensation that...well, it would have you reaching for the Dramamine, but you get the point.

Simply by re-thinking the need for a solid ride cart from front to back, they delivered an unprecedented ride experience. It's also noteworthy that this isn't something that Disney could do with a faster coaster for basically the same reason as the airplane example above. It's only because the mine train runs at a maximum of 34 MPH that such swaying is enjoyable. A significantly higher speed combined with a rocking motion would require a barf bag.

THE EXPERIENCE

Dwarfs, witches, and princesses come to life

THE TRICK

Some of the most advanced audio-animatronics in Disney history

While evaluating the replacement to Snow White's Scary Adventures, Disney execs deduced that status quo wouldn't be acceptable for the new attraction. They'd need to push themselves with regards to bringing the tale of Snow White's labor-intensive allies to life. Otherwise, park guests would view the new ride as a lateral move of sorts.

Imagineers went back to the drawing board and once again attacked an age-old problem. Audio-animatronics are ingrained as a key aspect of park lore, and Disney employees always feel driven to improve on the work of the innovators that came before them. In the case of Seven Dwarfs Mine Train, several upgrade opportunities presented themselves. They could add a layer of intrigue by casting shadows on the walls. This tactic would make the rider feel as if they're joining the Dwarfs on their journey. Several shiny barrels and sacks of gems would enhance the vibe of the glorified treasure hunt that drives the Dwarfs through the workday.

None of the above would matter if the Dwarfs themselves weren't lifelike, though. The problem Disney faced is that they didn't want to build entirely new audio-animatronics (AAs). They had a full set for the Snow White fairytale already; it'd be wasteful to dump those and start from scratch. This sense of pragmatism led to a clever design premise.

The outdated AAs could maintain utility if repositioned. Disney moved the proven, timeless AAs to a new location just before the end of the ride. To avoid concerns about the age of these character models, they employed obscured glass techniques to prevent excessive scrutiny of the not-quite-retired AAs. Through this tactic, they added a terrific set piece at a moment when people think the ride is over.

With the outdated AAs displayed elsewhere, Imagineers could flex their creative muscle by deploying new AAs. These stunningly life-like character models exemplify how far technology has come in the 2000s. While Disney constantly tweaks their existing attractions to keep them state-of-the-art, Seven Dwarfs Mine Train represented the first true step forward in AA technology in a generation of Disney attractions. And the results speak for themselves. The very first display has a special purpose in this regard. Doc's jeweled glasses show off the new technology and its stunning attention to detail.

That's not the greatest trick, though. That one is hidden in plain sight.The head of Disney's Parks & Resorts division, Tom Staggs, had a simple request. He asked for the most life-like Dwarfs possible, and while he loved the initial results, he wanted more. He realized that a realistic fairy tale character is a bit of a misnomer, which is why he went a different way. He requested that Snow White's worker bee buddies look like something more tangible. He asked for a set of characters that resembled something more iconic.

The next time you enjoy Seven Dwarfs Mine Train, pay attention to the look of the Dwarfs and see if they remind you of anything. They should. Disney modeled the 2014 version of the Seven Dwarfs after their original style, the one from the 1937 movie, Snow White and the Seven Dwarfs. In this manner, Disney looked forward with a new attraction that is the centerpiece of New Fantasyland. In doing so, they also paid homage to the movie that started it all for the company, a fitting tribute to their founder, Walt Disney.

CHAPTER TWENTY-FOUR

SOARIN' AROUND THE WORLD

In 2001, Disney California Adventure debuted to mixed reviews. Even the naysayers found something to love, though. From its inception, Soarin' Over California garnered a reputation as one of the greatest theme park attractions ever built. It masterfully re-created the sensation of hang gliding by using a unique ride apparatus to mimic the sensations of flight. The best part was that unlike most of the new attractions at California Adventure, its tie-in with the park theme was organic.

Theme park tourists who took a ride on Soarin' Airlines received a breathtaking view of some of California's natural wonders. Despite its West Coast specificity, Soarin' Over California was so popular that park planners took notice. They translated the ride to Walt Disney World's Epcot and then later announced plans to add an iteration of it at both Tokyo DisneySea and Shanghai Disneyland Park.

The catch was that a couple of issues existed. While many Walt Disney World guests know the landmarks of California, the same isn't true of Japanese or Chinese visitors. Disney strategists had to redesign Soarin' as a more global experience if they wanted it to expand its popularity abroad. From this point forward, multiple versions of the premise will exist, each of which is at least somewhat unique to its host park.

The primary one is known as Soarin' Around the World, and it became the talk of Epcot due to its spectacular innovations. Imagineers made changes under the hood, on screen, and even in the queue for the update. They had 15 years to think about what worked with the Soarin' concept as well as what needed improvement. Ultimately, they made revisions both huge and minuscule in updating the concept. What they wound up creating is another instant triumph worthy of discussion.

THE EXPERIENCE

Giving each of 87 passengers an optimal experience "in the air"

THE TRICK

Providing the sensation of flight

Imagineer Kathy Mangum described it thusly: "The genesis of the idea goes back to our dream of being able to fly, along with the impressive natural beauty of California" As originally envisioned, however, Soarin' was determined to be impossible by Disney Imagineers in 1996. The ride was initially conceptualized as a hang gliding simulator. The infamous "dry cleaning idea" presumed that individual seats would rotate on a moving conveyor, with guests hanging from hooks like laundry. Alas, designer Barry Braverman noted that it "had all kinds of problems." Presumably, theme park visitors don't enjoy feeling like they just came out of the dryer.

Several other strategies were examined, all of which had the same intended goal of giving the rider a great IMAX view plus the sensation of flight. None of them were deemed feasible. In the end, inspiration came from an unlikely source. Imagineer Mark Sumner happened to discover his childhood Erector Set during a weekend visit to his parents' house. While playing with his forgotten toys in the attic, Sumner was struck with inspiration. He returned to work with a functional design on the following Monday morning and promptly became known as Mr. Erector. Okay, nobody ever called him that, but his creative solution was immediately adopted.

The only difference between the model he displayed during that Monday meeting and the ride we have today is an apparatus built from a million pounds of steel capable of lifting 37 tons. The underlying design of the Erector Set prototype remains the same, though. Guests all board at once and then are simultaneously lifted to the appropriate level for their part of the IMAX viewing screen. It's an elegant solution to a seemingly impossible problem.

THE EXPERIENCE

Remaining true to the original vision for Soarin'

THE TRICK

Something old, something new

The problem Imagineers faced in re-imagining Soarin' is that they loved a lot about it. Many of them even lamented that they had to change from the popular storyline of the original. The sensations of flying through the grand mountains and breathtaking seas of the state of California still resonated 15 years later. Alas, not everything about Soarin' remained as fresh-scented as the Smellitzer fragrance of California orange groves.

Soarin' had a few areas for concern. The most important one was traffic flow. Park planners constantly stressed over attraction throughput, and that was an area where Soarin' had never excelled. While each ride apparatus hosts 87 guests, two theaters hold "only" 176 theme park tourists per showing. Including the loading and unloading time for these complex structures plus the 4:51 ride time, Soarin' could host approximately 1,200 guests per hour, 1,400 as a maximum. And that's why Soarin' always had one of the longest waits at Epcot.

A priority in renovating Soarin' was to fix this issue. Fortunately, it was easy to do, at least at Epcot. The attraction has always featured theaters on the left and right, and the park itself is notorious for open space. So, Disney added a third theater, Concourse C, which is straight ahead on the linear path rather than the turns to Concourses A and B. This modest improvement increased throughput by 50 percent without sacrificing anything. In fact, you should aim for Concourse C if you have the chance since the theater is 15 years newer. Since foot traffic is less of an issue at Disney California Adventure, park planners chose not to add any new theaters there.

As far as something old, Disney left a lot of the basics of Soarin' in place. They didn't tinker much with the lifting apparatus, which everyone considered an engineering triumph. They also understood the popularity of the pre-flight film starring Patrick Warburton as the chief flight attendant. The timeless aspect of his instructions and warnings required no updates, and people really love that bald guy with the mouse ears. Plus, the technical side, improved video resolution, doesn't apply to the line queue. So, Disney was able to keep its beloved Soarin' introduction. For older theme park tourists, Soarin' wouldn't be quite the same without it.

THE EXPERIENCE

Old ride, new destination

THE TRICK

Filming an entirely different movie

Since Disney wanted to present Soarin' to the world, they had to ditch the gorgeous California landscape. While nobody likes ditching a proven commodity, Imagineers felt a bit of liberation in the planning phase. Disneyland's home state claims countless impressive landmarks, but expanding their horizons added a whole new world, so to speak. Anything on Planet Earth was now available for potential placement in Soarin' 2: Electric Boogaloo.

Basically, Disney had its pick of the Seven Wonders of Nature and the New7Wonders of the World (the actual name coined by New7Wonders Foundation), plus any other parts of the world they felt would look majestic on camera. I would imagine that the arguments in these boardroom meetings were intense. Take a moment to think about the places you'd select. Now compare your list to others you find online. You'll quickly appreciate that universality of opinion is an impossibility with this exercise. Disney's Imagineers had to settle on a final list, even if the results were vociferously debated, and then film the international replacements for the visual highlights of California.

Disney was a bit cheeky with some of its selections. They chose the Matterhorn as a clever tribute to the world's first steel roller coaster, not coincidentally hosted at Disneyland. They also selected Sydney, Australia, for its dazzling harbor and world-renowned Sydney Opera House. Their tributes to the ancient wonders are the Great Wall of China and the Great Pyramids of Egypt. Natural landmarks such as Mount Kilimanjaro and Isfjord in Greenland are featured as well.

Imagineers also added more modern triumphs of architecture such as Neuschwanstein Castle in Germany, the Taj Mahal in India, and the Eiffel Tower in France. It's the last of these selections that has caused a bit of an uproar. Soarin' riders seated on the sides of the attraction rather than the middle have noticed a problem with the appearance of the Eiffel Tower. It leans. The one flaw Disney has yet to correct with Soarin' Around the World is that they've somehow managed to make the Eiffel Tower look more like the Leaning Tower of Pisa. It's an issue Disney expects to correct. Then again, they said the same thing about the Yeti at Expedition Everest.

Overall, Soarin' Over California highlighted 13 of the best locations in California, all of which were in a 770-mile region. Soarin' Around the World takes the rider on a worldwide tour of 13 different countries, all without requiring any luggage or a passport stamp. Also, Disney cleverly chose to end each trip at a different location. Whichever park you're visiting is also the last place you'll soar during the ride. Imagineers filmed special endings for Epcot, Disneyland, and Shanghai Disneyland.

THE EXPERIENCE

Bettering visuals that were sadly outdated

THE TRICK

15 years of HDTV improvements

Where to film wasn't the only integral part of the planning phase, either. In the 15 years since the original Soarin' had become a staple of Disney theme parks, video recording technology had expanded mightily. IMAX was a novelty at the turn of the millennium. Today, many mainstream cineplexes have one. IMAX movie revenue has become so prevalent that it is tracked as its own box office category.

As more cinematographers have worked with the technology, IMAX has improved technically and visually. Also, the entire world switched from film to digital over the time. In other words, the timing of Soarin' Over California was such that it just missed a new world of graphic storytelling.

In 2001, Disney employed the most established type of IMAX filming known at the time. Called IMAX HD, this style of filmmaking effectively tripled the clarity of 35mm frames. And it was HD by the conventional definition at the time, which was 1080p. That's probably the same as your first HDTV television or possibly slightly better if you owned 720p or 1080i. The problem is that an IMAX theater experience is supposed to blow away home viewing.

Soarin' Over California achieved this goal initially, but then it gradually degraded. I mean that literally. One of the principal criticisms of early IMAX was its artifacting. IMAX HD attempted to correct this by displaying at 48 frames per second, twice the cinematic standard. By the standards in place at the time, Soarin' offered state of the art visuals. But...

How far behind were visuals in 2001? Consider that one of the biggest videogames of that year was Halo. And I mean the original one. State of the art graphics at the time were along the lines of Final Fantasy X, a game that has since been remastered for the express purpose of improving its graphics. A more Disneyfied example would involve a comparison of Toy Story 2 to a Pixar release today. It's readily apparent how far the graphics technology has evolved in a relatively brief time. That's true of home theaters as well. Virtually no one had HDTV in the early days of Soarin', nor would they until a few years later. DVDs weren't even in their glory years yet. That wouldn't happen until 2005 and 2006.

Fast forward 15 years from the debut of Soarin'...

The world has changed in terms of visual expectations. Today, most homes have at least one HDTV, and the graphics on smartphones and tablets display visuals at a higher quality than televisions available a decade ago. Now think about Soarin', which used twin IMAX films to tell its story. Over time, those giant pieces of film (IMAX films platters used to weigh as much as 550 pounds) degraded. That's why the artifacting became such a problem over time. Theme park tourists at Disney California Adventure and Epcot would scoff at the lessened quality of the once-stunning visuals.

For the new version of Soarin', Disney once again employed the best IMAX product on the market. The difference is that it's not a relic that will quickly become outdated. When Imagineers developed Soarin' Over California, arguments were still ongoing about HDTV standards. Today, 4K isn't even widely adopted yet, but it's expected to become the standard for the next several years. The IMAX 4K Laser Projection System eliminates the need for ridiculously heavy film stock with digital files that are lossless, which is to say it's perfect video. Artifacting is a solved problem for the second version of Soarin'.

From the viewer perspective, Soarin' Around the World provides true HD imagery that's technically twice as good as the previous iteration. In reality, it's quite a bit better. 1080p and 2160p are just numbers. Other facets of the conversation such as aspect ratio and film rate (Soarin' still operates at 48fps, but 60fps is a possibility) factor in, but the most important one is that digital prints never age. This version will look example the same in 15 years, whereas the Soarin' Over California film prints became laughably degraded. The new iteration is twice the HD quality without dirty projection issues.

The result of all these improvements to the Soarin' premise is unmistakable. Soarin' Around the World absolutely dwarfs Soarin' Over California in terms of scope, scale, and visuals. While it's not perfect (yet), the advancements in technology over 15 years enabled Disney to tell a better story that covers the entire world rather than Disneyland's small (but wonderful) part of it. My only lament is that the orange grove smell is lost in the exchange. To me, that'll always be the greatest part of Soarin'.

CHAPTER TWENTY-FIVE

FROZEN EVER AFTER

Disney Imagineers are always up for a challenge. They've proven this since the early days, back when the idea of the Happiest Place on Earth was simply a thought bubble in Uncle Walt's head. Today's Imagineers face a challenge that the first generation of attraction architects couldn't imagine, though. On occasion, 21st century Imagineers must rebuild and repurpose existing rides and building spaces to craft original concepts.

The most famous recent example of this resides at the space once used for Maelstrom in the Norway Pavilion. This wonderful attraction dutifully entertained guests for more than 25 years. Sadly, it had one design flaw it couldn't overcome. It didn't feature either Elsa or Anna, the royal princesses of fictitious Arendelle, a place eerily similar in look and tone to Norway. Once *Frozen* became a global box office sensation, Maelstrom's fate was sealed, even though it had done nothing wrong.

In the wake of Disney's announcement to close Maelstrom forever, fans of the ride commiserated as they expressed horror about the decision. Disney was killing an iconic part of Epcot's World Showcase in favor of the flavor of the month, a decision they've since repeated with Guardians of the Galaxy. It was a business strategy, yes, but it also was a clever attempt to reinvigorate the World Showcase with a new attraction, something the company hadn't done since 2007 with the Gran Fiesta Tour Starring The Three Caballeros.

Frozen Ever After is a bold usage of the same space at the Norway Pavilion, and the first step toward reimagining the entire World Showcase for the 21st century. Let's go behind the ride to identify all the tricks of the trade Imagineers employed on Frozen Ever After. WARNING: This chapter will include spoilers about ride elements.

THE EXPERIENCE
Preventing the Maelstrom

THE TRICK
Killing two elements of the old attraction

While the *Frozen* license guaranteed instant popularity for the new ride, the conversion process came with its own difficulties. The primary challenge with Frozen Ever After was overcoming its limited space. The Maelstrom land didn't offer many good options for expansion.

The first step was choosing what could stay and what could go. A couple of hard calls were required. The first of them was to kill a unique element of Maelstrom. Cast members walled off the part of the ride that opened to the outdoors. This bit of construction prevented onlookers from getting a view of the boats from outside the attraction. It also turned Frozen Ever After into a literal dark ride, unlike the occasionally bright portion of Maelstrom.

Disney execs also quickly decided to toss out the post-Maelstrom movie, The Spirit of Norway. Functioning as a virtual time capsule by this point, the 1988 film was more than 25 years old and ridiculously dated. The celebration of pure Norwegian vocations such as sailing, fishing, and ski jumping (no, really) seemed like an Americanized perspective of the country akin to having an Australia Pavilion with a restaurant named Shrimp on the Barbie. Amazingly, the Norwegian government had input on every phase of this video, and that's why it's so cheesy that it circles back to fun. Even so, its removal barely caused a blip on the Disney fanatic radar. With the most Maelstrom-ish elements in mothballs, Imagineers could reboot the ride parts that remained.

THE EXPERIENCE
Turning Maelstrom into Frozen Ever After

THE TRICK
Repurposing and altering existing track

The company used this additional space in unexpected ways. Frozen Ever After's dimensions indicate that it has 964 feet of track, making it exactly the same length as Maelstrom. The placement of the track is different in some key locations, though. The loading section for Maelstrom is now where we see Olaf for the first time. Disney altered the previous unloading section so that it can handle loading duties as well. Changes like this seem trivial but are actually critical to the new version of the attraction.

Frozen Ever After features movie scenes. It's actually blocked that way. By changing the loading area and adding some curved track where the Maelstrom version had nothing else, Olaf can sing "Do You Want to Build a Snowman," setting the stage for the entirety of the attraction. Snow and ice are somewhat important to Elsa's story.

Imagineers had to get creative with the space they had. Otherwise, Frozen Ever After would feel rushed and incomplete. When they repurposed the track, they maintained almost all of the paths. The additions are crucial to the overall experience, though. Similarly, Disney added a couple of show pieces to enhance the pageantry and highlight the grandiose parts of Frozen Ever After. Palatial gates part to reveal the two seminal moments: Let It Go and the reunion of the sisters in their happily ever after poses. These seem like small inclusions for casual observers, but they build a mood and a feeling of expectation/excitement for the rider. The new doors are a wonderful example of the little touches that differentiate Disney from its imitators.

The rest of the track is similar, as are the beloved high spots carried over from Maelstrom. The 28-foot drop is still at the end, and the boats still turn backwards at one point before righting the ship (literally) just before the end. What's clever is that Disney leveraged these two moments to feature the biggest scene from *Frozen*, "Let It Go," and the most adorable characters, the tiny snowmen from *Frozen Fever*. The physical changing of direction of the Norwegian vessel synchronizes with fantastic story elements. It's another classic Disney touch.

The only flaw with using Maelstrom's old track and most of its loading system is throughput. Maelstrom could service a thousand guests an hour, and that was plenty for a hidden gem in the back of the World Showcase. Like Gran Fiesta Tour, it rarely had long line queues. A guest could jump out of the hot sun and enjoy a Viking sailing excursion in minutes.

A ride with the *Frozen* theme is a different story. A thousand guests per hour for Frozen Ever After is substandard throughput. In combination with frequent malfunctions, the wait for this attraction is rarely less than an hour. Ah well, what's an hour's wait to a guest when an epic rendition of Let It Go comes at the end?

THE EXPERIENCE

Re-creating the characters of *Frozen*

THE TRICK

The best audio-animatronics to date

Quick, when's the last time you remember Disney adding new audio-animatronics to a ride? You probably thought of Seven Dwarfs Mine Train, but that's kind of a cheat. Disney repurposed stuff they already had. They did this rather than building new Dwarfs from scratch. The reason is simple. It's much cheaper to update what you've already got. The Dwarfs you see on that attraction ARE improved, but they're not new.

Frozen Ever After can claim something special. The ride offers vastly superior audio-animatronics to any we've seen previously. The reason why is that technology has advanced dramatically since the last time Imagineers redefined the art of animatronics. They invented the craft in the 1950s and 1960s, but they've never stopped trying to perfect it. In the 21st century, the practice has received a boost from a long-awaited source.

Walt Disney himself dreamt of a world of functional robots. He even had a friend named Garco, a robot who cohosted the Disneyland television series during the 1950s. While talking machines were virtually non-existent during Uncle Walt's time, they've quickly become a part of everyday life in the smartphone era. Humans query artificial intelligence programs named Siri, Cortana, and Alexa millions of times each day. Meanwhile, experts in the field of robotics have worked to build machines that can mimic humans almost exactly. Imagineers have dabbled with robotics for decades now, and Frozen Ever After represents the culmination of their research.

The audio-animatronics for the denizens of Arendelle combine two techniques at once. The realistic faces of Anna, Elsa, and the gang are a product of projection. Thanks to bitmap projection, Imagineers can replicate features from Disney films (or anything else) onto uneven surfaces such as Cinderella Castle or Arendelle's royalty. The practice is the same. When you look at Olaf from any angle, his face will appear nearly identical to his CGI representation in Frozen. Thanks to this kind of asymmetrical CGI, audiences quickly buy into the premise that their Viking boat has transported them to the faraway land where Anna and Elsa are the benevolent rulers.

While you appreciate the faces, Disney moves the bodies thanks to state-of-the-art robotics. Frozen Ever After's characters claim historically unprecedented movement abilities. The mechanical parts of the audio-animatronics have a flow that is almost perfectly realistic...or at least as realistic as there can be for a living snowman. When Anna and Elsa hold hands at the end of the ride, any sense of artificiality is absent from the proceedings. That's in stark contrast to classic audio-animatronics from even just a few years ago such as Captain Jack Sparrow on Pirates of the Caribbean. At this moment, Frozen Ever After has the best audio-animatronics ever built. But that target is always moving at Disney theme parks.

THE EXPERIENCE

A chilly visit to Arendelle

THE TRICK

A real world re-creation of moments from *Frozen*

One other element of the ride track required fundamental change. Maelstrom told an engaging story of Norwegian fables, including an ill-behaved troll. Frozen Ever After tells a story about the happily ever after that two sisters enjoy in the wake of the events of *Frozen* (and *Frozen Fever*). The way that Maelstrom was blocked, timing was important. Otherwise, riders would miss some of the corresponding audio. The way that Frozen Ever After works, timing is *everything*.

As previously mentioned, Imagineers tell the Frozen story in blocks. Think of them as scenes akin to a movie. The introductory scene is especially thematic. A creature made of ice sings, "Do you want to build a snowman?" It sets the tone for a chilly trip through the mountains of Arendelle. Then, you meet trolls, but these are not the ones from Maelstrom. They're kindly creatures who helped to raise Kristoff back in the day. Later, you get to watch Kristoff sing a duet with his beloved, Anna. Along the way, you meet a reindeer who has pulled a Flick from *A Christmas Story*. His tongue stretches helplessly against an icy pole. All of these scenes re-create popular moments from the movie in a more realistic way than ever before at a Disney theme park. Frozen Ever After is a (successful) attempt to place the rider in the movie for a few minutes.

THE EXPERIENCE

A powerful rendition of "Let It Go"

THE TRICK

Structuring the ride around *Frozen*'s famous song

The signature moment is exactly what you'd expect, too. Earlier in the ride, guests approach an ice castle, heightening the anticipation for the seminal moment. Once the vessel barges through the aforementioned palatial gates, they see Elsa for the first time. She bursts into song. You know the one.

Even though "Let It Go" isn't precisely the halfway point of the ride, it still feels like that's the intent. The moments prior to "Let It Go" are an introduction to the beloved characters of Frozen. After Elsa, the boat sails backwards down an icy mountain river. The experience is almost as if Disney is letting the rider catch their breath after the dazzling rendition of the iconic song.

The scene with the performance of "Let It Go" is the highlight of Frozen Ever After. It's probably also the pitch that sold Disney execs on the idea of rebooting Maelstrom. The musical re-creation of this moment includes amazing staging. As the boat enters the area, Elsa dominates the point of view, but the room offers plenty more to enjoy. Adjoining projections on side walls emphasize the icy nature of Elsa's castle. Fittingly, frozen fractals are all around as the ship approaches the stunning Snow Queen.

The audio ascends as Idina Menzel's inimitable voice tears through the lyrics of the best Disney movie song of the 21st century (if not ever). This is Elsa's moment, and Imagineers extended it as much as they could. The trip down the mountain includes images of ice, snowflakes, and Elsa. They're little more than an excuse to extend the song as much as possible during a ride that's exactly five minutes. And that brings us back to the timing.

Imagine how the showpiece of "Let It Go" would seem if the timing were inexact. Since Frozen Ever After features several musical performances, the boats have to "sail" to the correct spot at the right moment. There's no give here like Imagineers had with Maelstrom. The reason why Disney required almost two years to build Frozen Ever After is that they had to modify the tracks. Yes, they had the apparatus in place, but they had to update it so that the timing of each boat was precise to the microsecond. That's also one of the main reasons why the attraction breaks down so often. Anything that significantly disrupts the timing of a Viking boat triggers a shutdown. It's a small price to pay to enjoy the majesty of the center stage rendition of "Let It Go," though.

Finally, here's one miscellaneous note for you lovers of Maelstrom. Disney cast members felt a bit guilty about shuttering such a beloved ride. They felt it had nobly represented the great nation of Norway for many years and wanted to honor it. When they constructed the accompanying Arendelle Sommerhus, Imagineers removed the rune stones from Maelstrom and placed them at the entrance to the new area.

CHAPTER TWENTY-SIX

GUARDIANS OF THE GALAXY—MISSION: BREAKOUT!

Change is inevitable, especially at Disneyland. The place that Uncle Walt built operates under a simple edict. Its founder once proclaimed, "Disneyland will never be completed. It will continue to grow as long as there is imagination left in the world."

Even half a century after his death, Disney's edict has placed constant pressure on Imagineers. They know their leader's expectations for the park that bears his name. They feel compelled to honor Disney's stated desire about Disneyland. And that's how unprecedented change arrives at the Happiest Place on Earth.

One example came in early 2017, when Disney California Adventure unexpectedly shuttered one of its most popular and beloved attractions, the Twilight Zone Tower of Terror. That same "tower" would shut down long enough to receive a new theme, one that prioritized superheroes over the supernatural. In only a few short months, Imagineers converted something wonderful into an attraction that many feel is superior. Let's take this opportunity to go behind the ride to learn how Guardians of the Galaxy—Mission: Breakout! rose from the ashes of Twilight Zone Tower of Terror.

THE EXPERIENCE
Replacing a tower with a collection

THE TRICK
A new coat of paint

The striking part of Disney's announcement about the closure of the Twilight Zone Tower of Terror was the timeline given.

The Rod Serling masterpiece would operate for the final time on January 3, 2017. The intended launch of its replacement was roughly the same time as the release of the second movie in the franchise, Guardians of the Galaxy 2, which opened on May 5, 2017.

The seemingly impossible schedule allowed Imagineers only four months to create something entirely new. Sure, they would repurpose many of the existing elements of the building, but the stated deadline was brutal. To their credit, cast members effectively reconstructed the drop tower dark ride in only four months and 22 days. Basically, Disney built an entirely new ride in a single semester. No pressure, college students!

In order to have an entirely new ride ready within five months, Imagineers obviously had to make some sacrifices. They couldn't fundamentally alter the structure of the building. It would remain a drop tower ride, but the style and tone would change almost overnight.

The original version of the attraction was a gothic take on an abandoned hotel, a building that somehow existed in an alternate dimension. The modified take on the premise is in our dimension...but it is entire galaxies away. And I mean it when I say that the primary difference on a surface level is a new coat of paint.

Disney modified the façade of the tower, eliminating the darker tones in favor of extremely bright colors and oddly alien designs. These cosmetic changes were easy to achieve but changed the perception of the attraction from a distance.

The new tower is inviting rather than foreboding.

Guardians of the Galaxy—Mission: Breakout! is like one of those makeover montages from teen romantic comedies. The dorky shell of Twilight Zone, the part that Disney wanted left in the past, was discarded in favor of a new outfit that forced everyone to reevaluate their preconceived notions of the tower. The addition of a few shiny baubles changed more than just a building façade. It also hinted at a dramatically different Disney California Adventure in the offing...

THE EXPERIENCE

The first true Disney-built Marvel superhero ride in North America

THE TRICK

A more modern theme befitting its titular comic book team

When the Disney company purchased Marvel Entertainment in 2009, theme park analysts expressed confusion over the transaction. After all, Universal Studios owned airtight rights to the primary Marvel comic book superheroes in perpetuity at Walt Disney World. What would Disney get out of the transaction?

That question returned a shocking answer. Disney intended to build its own new set of iconic superheroes. They mined the vast Marvel back catalog to unearth a team that would check off all the boxes for a popular Disney character. They needed cute and adorable heroes to sell toys, but they also needed plausible warriors to anchor the team. With the *Guardians of the Galaxy*, Disney struck gold in both ways. They sold plenty of Groot and Rocket Raccoon merchandise while simultaneously elevating Chris Pratt to superstardom as Star Lord.

These newly adored Marvel characters weren't tethered to the same contract constrictions as many of The Avengers, giving Disney full reign to use them at North American parks. The company did just that in renovating the Tower of Terror space for its new heroes. In the process, they hinted at a future version of Disney California Adventure (DCA) that wholly sidestepped the park's original theme, California, in favor of licensed characters from Disney's massive intellectual property library. The DCA of tomorrow is a blissful marriage of Marvel and Pixar.

To reach that point, Disney had to start somewhere, and their first step forward was into a new galaxy. After the shocking success of Guardians of the Galaxy in 2014, Disney execs felt confident that they'd found the perfect property to reboot not just Tower of Terror but DCA in its entirety. They embarked on a daring plan to shoot extra scenes during the filming of the sequel. The cast of *Guardians of the Galaxy 2*, including new additions such as Mantis, also comprises the cast of Mission: Breakout!

This new footage would become the basis for a Guardians of the Galaxy attraction. It would mirror aspects of the second film; however, Disney went out of its way to note that the story told on the ride would vary slightly from the two films. Yes, Mission: Breakout! exists in its own private Marvel universe. If you see anything that conflicts with the story of the two films, that's intentional. The attraction stands on its own as a singularly unique comic book adventure. But it absolutely drills the tone and style of the two films. For example...

THE EXPERIENCE

A six-song soundtrack that determines your trajectory

THE TRICK

Six song-based variations of the same general ride experience

From the first trailer, *Guardians of the Galaxy* hooked its target audience on a feeling. That first commercial employed an AM Radio classic by Blue Swede to set the mood for the weirdness of the guardians themselves. An unconventional superhero team, they are led by a kid whose mind is sort of stuck in a late-1970s time warp. The music of that era defines part of his personality.

In the movie sequel, Star Lord aka Peter Quill evolves a bit, or at least lets time catch up to him. Some of his music advances into the 1980s, the MTV era. And several of those tracks populate the list of ride possibilities on Mission: Breakout!

Whereas Tower of Terror had a sort of randomness to its elevator chutes, the Guardians of the Galaxy version has a tell. When you hear the first notes of the music play, you know exactly which of the six variations of the ride that you're about to experience. The action onscreen will mirror the musical accompaniment to an extent. Some of the cinematics are only available when certain music tracks play. In other words, the audio drives the video more than the reverse.

Those six songs are:

- "Hit Me with Your Best Shot" by Pat Benatar
- "Give Up The Funk" by Parliament
- "Born to Be Wild" by Steppenwolf
- "I Want You Back" by the Jackson 5
- "Free Ride" by the Edgar Winter Group
- "Burning Love" by Elvis Presley

And yes, that's quite the eclectic mix. Guardians of the Galaxy director James Gunn actually had rare input on the selections. He suggested the music that would best fit the tone of each ride trajectory. The soundtrack is a reflection of the journey, just as is true for Peter Quill in the movie franchise.

From a rider perspective, knowing the song will give you a sense of familiarity about repeated trips through Mission: Breakout! The instant the guitar riff triggers for "Hit Me With Your Best Shot," you know that Baby Groot is about to get everyone else in trouble. For "Free Ride," you'll jump into the middle of an outer space firefight. Each iteration has a musical identifier, something that's never been done an attraction previously. Disney wanted to give the Guardians of the Galaxy attraction something special, and they fittingly chose music for the backbone of the journey.

THE EXPERIENCE

You battle the Collector to escape from his fortress

THE TRICK

Old-fashioned Disney theming with a modern techy spin

The ride itself is much more structured than Tower of Terror. For the original version, Disney told the backstory via a monologue and a video introduction from Rod Serling. It was awesome, but it was also a bit dated.

Mission: Breakout! uses a different storytelling structure. The scenes filmed especially for the attraction drive the action. The experience is kinetic for the viewer since so much action is taking place right in front of them...while they're bouncing up and down. Still, it's a structurally sound story, a Guardians of the Galaxy short film, if you will.

Disney doesn't do anything special on this part of the attraction. Instead, Imagineers returned to basics. They used classic tricks integrated with new technology to build something new and original.

The story is that a nefarious villain named the Collector has attempted to trap the Guardians of the Galaxy, making them permanent residents of the Tivan Collective. Our heroes ain't having it and plan to escape. Notably, the worker bees in the

Collector's employ are on the side of the Guardians. They too were captured and enslaved here and want to do their part to help everyone break out. As you stand in the line queue, you'll hear whispers and hints from disembodied voices.

At the actual start of the ride, Rocket Raccoon (in animated form) announces his plan. He's going to shut down the power on the cages, giving everyone a chance to escape. What follows is a crazed race to the generator room and a few choice encounters with monsters. The tentacle creature from Guardians of the Galaxy 2 is in most iterations, but a gargoyle and a rat thing also make appearances in some variations. You may even encounter multiple monsters on your ride!

The entire experience plays out like a classic Hollywood action scene. Stuff gets shot, clever lines of heroism get recited, and everyone inevitably makes it out in one piece...save for the tentacle monster, who really needs a better agent.

The beauty of Guardians of the Galaxy—Mission: Breakout! is that it fulfills a promise offered long ago by the original Star Tours. This revamped tower ride actually feels like a Choose Your Own Adventure set to rock music. Each iteration is slightly different in storytelling, but the sensation is still the same.

You bounce up and down in an elevator shaft, just as you always did on Twilight Zone Tower of Terror. The difference is that there is now a giant digital monitor in front of you, and it offers a mirrored onscreen video accompaniment to your springing up and down. It's a subtle but brilliant themed illusion that modernizes many of Disney's classic Imagineering tricks.

Disney didn't reinvent the wheel with Guardians of the Galaxy—Mission: Breakout!, but I would argue that they did perfect it.

CHAPTER TWENTY-SEVEN

AVATAR FLIGHT OF PASSAGE

Disney park planners felt tremendous pressure to build something magnificent with Pandora. Sure, the company always has lofty standards for its Parks & Resorts division, but they felt hyper-competitive with this themed land. It was, whether Disney will admit it or not, a direct response to the ultra-successful Wizarding World of Harry Potter. Pandora had to raise the bar for a new themed land so that Disney could establish dominance once again. The ride that is integral to this goal is the E ticket attraction at Pandora. Let's go behind the ride yet again to learn about Imagineering triumph that is Avatar Flight of Passage.

THE EXPERIENCE

Six hours in line...the fun way!

THE TRICK

The longest line queue ever built

Plenty of debate on the internet involves the lingering impact of *Avatar*. At one point, it was the number one North American movie of all-time. At the time of publication, it's still the global box office champion. Suffice to say that Avatar sold a metric ton of movie tickets, domestically and internationally.

When Disney announced the Pandora expansion in 2011, they projected huge crowds, especially given what was happening with the Wizarding World of Harry Potter. A few years later, the idea that *Avatar* would appeal to customers as much as Harry Potter seems a bit silly. Still, the crowds at Avatar Flight of Passage are roughly what Disney had projected.

In order to host all that traffic, the attraction had to have a massive line queue...and it does. While the need isn't there most of the time (thank heavens), this line can service six hours' worth of traffic! Even this long after its debut, Flight of Passage still has a two-hour wait on most days. That's a lot of guests who would feel bored if the wait weren't engaging.

Disney addressed this by building *the* best line queue of all-time. As you walk through the line, you'll see a story told in several phases. As you may know, Pandora: The World of Avatar takes place long after the wars between humankind and Na'vi are over.

The backdrop is a previous Resources Development Administration mining facility, the kind seen in the first movie, which means it has military stuff. After the war, it becomes the Pandora Conservation Initiative's Mountain Banshee Project, a research facility. As you wander the halls, you'll see remnants of the war-torn Pandora of yesteryear, which feels incongruous with the current high-tech science center.

Disney's attention to detail on the theming is so precise that the outer portions of the facility are dilapidated. Trees and vines grow on the walls where once humans had held down the fort while mining Unobtanium. The electrical equipment is all rusted after decades without usage. Then, the colors come alive as the queue enters the bioluminescent portion of the mine. Finally, guests approach the line in the middle of the facility, and there they see...

THE EXPERIENCE

A realistic and immersive science center

THE TRICK

High-tech gadgets and a scarily realistic Na'vi avatar in a tube

The final section of the queue is futuristic and high-tech. It's where scientists honor the work of Dr. Grace Augustine from Avatar, which is to say it's home to the Avatar Program. Here, people see eight-foot-tall blue striped Na'vi up close.

The most famous of these Na'vi is the one I call Test Tube Guy. When you enter the final portion of the line queue, you'll see an Imagineered re-creation of one of the Avatars from the film. While this isn't technically the same one called Jake Sully in the film, it's cosmetically indistinguishable.

Disney worked hand in hand with James Cameron to get the look and feel right on the test tube Na'vi. The water in the giant tube even bubbles appropriately. This animatronic isn't as animated as you might expect; it basically just sits in the tube and looks all Avatar-y. Still, it's somehow awesome due to the lifelike detail. When you watch it, you'll believe that you're looking at an Avatar that could come to life at any second.

THE EXPERIENCE

Feeling like you're a part of the Avatar Program

THE TRICK

Building the Genetic Matching Room

One of the most inventive parts of the ride happens just before you board Flight of Passage. The Genetic Matching Room is where you watch the pre-flight videos that are basically informational in nature. Since not everyone is familiar with the world of Pandora, Disney offers two different instructional videos about how the ride will work. These clips add depth to the story of Avatar, and they also alert people to the novel nature of the attraction.

To hide the extended bouts of narration, Disney offers some clever sleight of hand. This area also hosts the Genetic Matching Room, a shiny distraction that seems incredibly futuristic. A scanner examines your body and then chooses the perfect Avatar for your body type. This choice will vary with repeated rides, and it does impact your flight, at least slightly. More importantly, you'll feel more engaged since the genetic matching process makes you feel connected to your Avatar, much like Jake Sully in the film.

THE EXPERIENCE

Bringing the world of Avatar to life

THE TRICK

Following the advice of James Cameron

When Disney approached *Avatar* creator James Cameron about an E Ticket attraction, he had a simple request. He wanted "Soarin' over Pandora." That may seem ridiculous in theory since you know that Flight of Passage is an augmented reality ride on an individual ride cart that's basically a motorcycle seat. That sounds nothing like Soarin', right? Well...

The similarities between the two attractions are unmistakable once you know the tricks, and you're about to learn them right now. Disney did construct Flight of Passage as a kindred spirit to Soarin'. They weren't about to duplicate the ride, of course, as people expect more from a Disney attraction. As such, the similarities are subtle rather than overt.

The first one is that the ride carts are on different levels. You won't notice the feet of people flying above you as with Soarin', but the premise is similar. To offer as much throughput as possible, Imagineers constructed the attraction room to have a tiered stage.

As for the ride cart, it's a contraption that sweeps everyone into the air the way that Soarin' does, but it mimics the sensation of flight in a similar way. Disney uses augmented (not virtual) reality to create the illusion that theme park tourists are riding creatures that are called Ikran, aka banshees.

Cameron describes it this way: "You know, riding the Ikran is a thrill. You're going to plunge. You're going to dive. You're going to swoop. It's like dreaming with your eyes open."

Imagineer Joe Rohde adds, "In Flight of Passage, the sensation of flying is really visceral, really believable. Not only do you have the more obvious aspects of flying—the swooping and curving—but we've put in crosswind, air density and banking."

Riding a banshee is no different than flying on a hang glider. You're still hundreds of feet in the air, getting a sense of the world in a way that humans can't on their own. Since Pandora is an alien world, the experience seems different, but the structure is similar. You see a giant projection screen in front of you, and the ride twists and turns based on the screen imagery. And since it's an Avatar ride, OF COURSE it's in 3D. The augmented reality goggles add depth to the realms of Pandora, making all forms of life seem that much more realistic and, in some instances, dangerously close.

That's not the last Soarin' trick, either. Disney again uses piped-in smells to accentuate the ride. In the original version of Soarin', oranges added to the illusion that you were flying through orange groves. During Flight of Passage, you'll start to smell ember as you approach a volcano. You'll also receive a gentle spray as you approach the water, another bit transferred from Soarin'. Clearly, the ride is more than just the inspiration for Flight of Passage. It's a kindred spirit and direct predecessor.

In a way, Flight of Passage is a modern version of Soarin', which seems odd since Disney just rebooted Soarin' in 2016. Still, James Cameron's vision for the ride included that Soarin' structure, only made to feel more modern thanks to an immersive ride experience based on augmented reality. The signature attraction at Pandora—The World of Avatar takes some of the best ideas from an incredible attraction and elevates them using state-of-the-art technology. It's easy to understand why Avatar Flight of Passage is one of the most critically praised new attractions of the 21st century. It's an instant classic.

CHAPTER TWENTY-EIGHT

NA'VI RIVER JOURNEY

Disney loves its theme park boat rides. The most famous ones are It's a Small World, Jungle Cruise, and Pirates of the Caribbean, of course, but they've built several others such as Living with the Land, Storybook Land Canal Boats, and Gran Fiesta Tour Starring the Three Caballeros. These attractions are one of their core concepts, as they provide a gentle ride with steady traffic throughput.

When Imagineers planned their latest themed land expansion, Pandora: The World of Avatar, they appreciated the advantages of a new boat ride. They could display the spectacular bioluminescent special effects that permeate throughout Pandora. Also, this sort of attraction could siphon some of the traffic off the streets, keeping the crowds under control. Most importantly, it was a major attraction that Disney could use as a selling point for their high-priced expansion.

You've heard all about it for years now. Let's take this opportunity to go behind the ride to learn four amazing aspects of Na'Vi River Journey.

THE EXPERIENCE

A journey through the heart of Pandora

THE TRICK

Building another unforgettable boat ride

Imagineers have crafted so many boat rides over the years because they're extremely functional. The water rides are gentle and breezy for park guests, i.e. they're comfortable.

For Disney, they're controllable. Cast members know where each person will be throughout the ride. With a large enough man-made river, they can flood the seas with boats, too, thereby servicing hundreds of park guests simultaneously. Disney hosts six to eight guests on each vessel, which means the rides aren't as populated as It's a Small World or Pirates of the Caribbean. Disney makes it up in volume instead. That's the functional side, but it's not why park planners loved the idea of a boat ride at Pandora, though.

Since the announcement of the themed land expansion in 2011, Disney dreamt big about their new land. They understood that the waters of Pandora are important in the movie, Avatar, and they wanted to re-create that experience. They used the boat ride as the means to give guests an unprecedented view of the world of Pandora, so that people would feel like they were exploring it just as Jake Sully once had.

Theoretically, theme park tourists are on a canoe ride down the sacred Kaspavan River, which is part of the Mo'ara Valley's rainforest. By using boats, Disney can show action and scenes at the various set pieces on this Na'Vi River Journey. And they have several tricks up their sleeve to achieve this goal...

THE EXPERIENCE

Beauty as far as the eye can see

THE TRICK

Bioluminescence throughout the journey

In speaking of Pandora prior to its opening, Disney executives sounded unusually confident. They'd seen the aspects of the land that would differentiate it from anything that had come before...at Disney or anywhere else.

People familiar with *Avatar* the movie know that one of the distinguishing characteristics is the colorful illumination. Director James Cameron wanted to introduce creatures that would emphasize the beauty of the then-nascent 3D technology. He settled on bioluminescent ones, with the result being the most popular global release of all-time. Movie-goers loved *Avatar* for its breathtaking visuals. Disney wasn't about to slack on the themed land that mirrors it.

And that leads to the logical question. What's bioluminescence? There's a simple, not-too-science-y answer to this, too. These are lights produced by living organisms. Some creatures emit this light as part of a biochemical reaction. When you hear the phrase bioluminescence, what you're really hearing is bugs, plants and animals that naturally create light. And you've seen an example of bioluminescence your whole life. You just didn't know the name.

The most famous such creatures are fireflies and jellyfish, but literally thousands of other examples are likely to exist. Most of them are underwater, a place mankind just now understands thanks to new camera innovations, some of which were championed by...James Cameron. So, he's legitimately one of the world's foremost experts on bioluminescence and someone Imagineers could lean on while spitballing ideas. And these discussions led to...

THE EXPERIENCE

Shiny animals frolicking in their "natural" environments

THE TRICK

Integrating set pieces and projection TVs to bring Pandora to life

The canoe ride down the Kaspavan River is magical due to Disney's presentation of the various set pieces. Some of the constructs are real pieces that you can reach out and touch. These elements like mushrooms and flying fan lizards provide the backdrop for the ride, but they do more. They also provide the artificial illumination that brightens the path through the darkness.

Disney re-created many of the creatures seen in the movie for this reason. The animals add to the illusion that you're taking a tourist cruise on an exotic planet. According to the Avatar wiki, the list of bioluminescent and native animals of Pandora includes hexapedes, prolemuris, panoprya, and sturmbeests, plus the flying fan lizards and woodsprites. During the ride, you're most likely to notice the lizards since they seem like spinning discs, but everything has a purpose straight down to the mushrooms.

To accentuate the perception of a real trip through Pandora, Disney uses video projection mapping akin to what you've seen in the Happily Ever After fireworks exhibition. As you drive past certain points, you'll see Na'Vi hunters and some of the most dangerous fauna in the background. It's an adrenaline surge on an otherwise laid back ride.

Disney even pulls out one of its oldest tricks to bring Pandora to life. Some of the leaves above the boats have shadows on them. The blue of the vegetation meshes with the black shadows to create a specific illusion. It looks like creatures are walking on the leaves. Since this vegetation is basically on the ceiling, such a thing is impossible. Imagineers again use projection to cast these skittering shadows. They make every "living" creature on Na'Vi River Journey seem real, especially...

THE EXPERIENCE

A Na'Vi spiritual leader welcomes you to her humble abode

THE TRICK

The most realistic audio-animatronic (AA) ever created

The climax of Na'Vi River Journey sees the boat reach its destination, the Na'vi Shaman of Song. She's currently leading a hymn whose lyrics are discussed in the next section. This audio-animatronic reflects a decade of technological innovations that surpass what was universally regarded as the best previous one, the famously broken Disco Yeti.

In the 11 years between the construction of the two AAs, computer advances gave Imagineers unprecedented leeway in building the Shaman of Song. Her movements are the most fluid of any AA to date. She also has countless simultaneous moving parts. When you see her, you may feel overwhelmed in choosing which part of her to watch. Both of her hands have individual gestures rather than symmetrical ones. Her tail flicks like a frisky cat, and she gyrates as she sings her song. It's stunningly life-like, although the Shaman is also gigantic at almost 10-feet-tall.

THE EXPERIENCE

A soulful rendition of the Na'Vi people's favorite hymn

THE TRICK

A new language and a terrific sound system

Sounds play throughout the ride, first standard jungle noises that highlight how native beasts communicate, then about a minute into the journey, tribal music begins to play, and it rises to a crescendo as guests approach the Song of Shaman.

Her song is important, although you won't understand it. Cameron hired a linguist to build an entire Na'Vi language. Dr. Paul Frommer then had the honor of crafting the companion song for Na'Vi River Journey. While the song is in Pandoran, he was kind enough to provide a translation of the final version, even as he noted that he'd written several different iterations of the lyrics. He wrote the first set more than two years prior to the opening of Pandora, which speaks volumes about the level of preparation required for an attraction of this scale.

Here are the translated lyrics of the Shaman's Song:

Stanza One:
O beautiful forest,
There are tears in the forest.
Woodsprite(s).
We cry out, calling,
"O Eywa!" (3X)

Stanza Two:
Connected as one,
O Great Mother.
Woodsprite(s).
We cry out, calling,
"O Eywa!" (3X)

Stanza Three:
By the People's will,
the forest is singing.
Woodsprite(s).
We cry out, calling,
"O Eywa!" (3X)

Disney had a simple goal in constructing Na'Vi River Journey. Famous Imagineer Joe Rohde describes it as, "Just plain beauty." When you ride it, you'll appreciate how the Imagineering tricks listed here elevate it to something spectacular. The attraction has the task of accentuating all the spectacular sights of Pandora, and it does this in a subtle, almost poetic way. While Avatar Flight of Passage gets most of the headlines, Na'Vi River Journey is the better example of life in Pandora.

CHAPTER TWENTY-NINE

THE INCREDICOASTER

How do you improve something that's already great? That's the question Imagineers faced when Disney repurposed California Screamin'. It wasn't just the best roller coaster at Disneyland; it was one of the best attractions overall. Making California Screamin' better wasn't easy, but the park planners at Disney California Adventure somehow managed. Let's go behind the ride to learn the tricks that turned the Incredicoaster into the most wonderful new ride at the Happiest Place on Earth!

THE EXPERIENCE

A repurposed California Screamin'

THE TRICK

New paint, new lights, and a lot of great ideas

Disney California Adventure (DCA) struggled from the beginning. Its questionable theme, the state of California, failed to attract guests from near or far. Californians could see the state from their living room, and tourists didn't want to visit a theme park simulation of something that they could experience for real in other places.

Over the years, DCA dwindled in popularity, particularly in comparison with its adjoining park, Disneyland. Disney executives tried to improve the lesser gate, and they gained momentum with Radiator Springs Racers. Even with the addition of that tremendous themed land, park planners knew that DCA needed to change. Ultimately, that change required new theming. The California core concept dwindled, with a replacement of Pixar and Marvel themed attractions.

California Screamin' had won over even the most diehard DCA critics with its glorious adrenaline rush. This roller coaster stood apart from the largely generic crop of attractions at the park. Still, it had California right there in the title, and its coolest trick involved circling through the Paradise Pier logo that highlighted the park. That seemed brilliant right up until the moment that Disney chose to change said logo to Pixar Pier. They needed a roller coaster that reflected this fundamental redesign of DCA.

In January of 2018, park officials revealed that California Screamin' would close forever, and the Incredicoaster would rise from its ashes. With such a limited amount of time to redesign the attraction, the repurposed roller coaster would share most major similarities with its predecessor. Disney would make up the difference with its special skill, immaculate theming.

Almost all of the changes from California Screamin' are cosmetic. The length of the track is still 6,072 feet, and the coaster carts still zoom along the tracks at 55 miles per hour, reaching that speed in only four seconds. It's the small stuff that changes everything, though...

THE EXPERIENCE

Entering the world of the Parr family

THE TRICK

Telling a story worthy of The Incredibles franchise

In the summer of 2018, *The Incredibles 2* scored the box office record for the largest Pixar opening weekend ever, the most popular Pixar domestic release ever, *and* the most popular animated movie of all time in North America. Alas, Disney didn't know any of this back in 2017 when they started plotting out the plans for the Incredicoaster. They had seen early footage of the film, however, and they knew that the concept was terrific. To a larger point, they believed in the Parrs.

The Parr family is the backbone of the Incredibles. It's a husband-and-wife super-team that agrees to stop fighting crime and raise a family. What they should have expected is that people born with super powers tend to have children who have super powers. Violet Parr, the oldest child, has the powers of invisibility and force field generation. Dashiell Parr aka the

Dash is lightning fast. Both of their abilities pale in comparison to the baby of the family.

Jack-Jack Parr, the youngest of the three children in the film, is the most extreme example. He doesn't have a single superpower. He has more than 15 of them! And this surprise reveal is the impetus for the attraction.

On the Incredicoaster, you're trying to catch Jack-Jack. Disney has themed the entire attraction around the idea that Jack-Jack has escaped from his babysitter. From the moment that you hear the voice of Edna Mode lamenting the missing baby, the attraction engulfs you in Incredibles theming. The covered sections that blocked the sun on California Screamin' have added new features now. They're an organic part of the storytelling!

This particular Imagineering trick is one that exemplifies Disney's creative solutions. With California Screamin', they had a set piece of track and an inability to modify the ride structure. They looked at the attraction with fresh eyes and had an epiphany. The tunnels had modest utility in their current forum. With a few clever changes, however, they could become set pieces that revealed the story sequentially.

Yes, Disney has introduced new set pieces within the tunnels of the Incredicoaster. In the first section, the ceiling has laser beams on it! They're not randomly positioned there. They indicate that Jack-Jack has discharged laser beams from his eyes. For the Parr family, these lasers operate as a tracking device. They know that the baby went thataway! From a rider perspective, they're a colorful addition that jazzes up the tunnel interiors.

Other tunnels similarly advance the plot. Bob Parr punches through a wall in a failed attempt to retrieve his youngest son. Helen Parr stretches more than 60 feet as she tries to grab Jack-Jack. This set piece is the longest of its kind that Disney has ever designed. Alas, Jack-Jack goes gooey, another fun visual. It's a "blink and you'll miss it" image, though. Later, Violet tries to project a force shield around her brother. Again, the family's attempt is unsuccessful.

Every section of the old California Screamin' is now an integral part of the story of the Incredicoaster. Once you exit the tunnels, the tone will change into something more playful. Jack-Jack has displayed his last trick. He can turn into multiple Jack-Jacks! Several of him will pop up as you streak through the bunny hops toward the end of the roller coaster.

THE EXPERIENCE

Trying to catch a super-baby at 55mph

THE TRICK

Simulating a high-speed chase in a controlled environment

The sensations of the twists and turns of California Screamin' were delightful on their own. With the Incredicoaster upgrades, they add to the feeling of urgency that you must grab Jack-Jack before something unfortunate happens to him or, more likely, someone else.

From the moment that Dash begins the countdown to start the chase, you feel like you're on a timer. You have a set amount of time to catch the baby. The catch is that the baby can defend himself in many, many ways. By switching the ride to this simple premise, the roller coaster swaps from pointless, glorious fun to a thrilling, purposeful mission. You're a hero trying to save a baby!

The lingering tracks from the old ride are now the path that takes you to Jack-Jack. You encounter him multiple times on the ride, narrowly missing during each one. You have him in sight throughout the Incredicoaster, but he's devilishly clever at picking the perfect superpower to escape you.

The theming fundamentally alters the dynamic of the repurposed coaster. And that's what makes it such a triumphant feat of Imagineering. They've enhanced an already exceptional thrill ride into a themed masterpiece. You'll feel the intensity of both the ride and the mission as you pursue the world's most powerful baby. Somehow, it's an adrenaline rush *and* a story about family. That's precisely what a ride based on The Incredibles franchise should be.

CHAPTER THIRTY

SLINKY DOG DASH

Have you ridden Slinky Dog Dash yet? If not, "you are a sad, strange little man and you have my pity." The hottest new ride at Disney's Hollywood Studios isn't an E-Ticket attraction per se. It's more of a family-friendly roller coaster that fills a niche. Still, it's the anchor attraction at Toy Story Land, the themed land that's driving attendance at Walt Disney World right now. It uses a lot of impressive Imagineering tricks, too. Let's go behind the ride to learn what makes Slinky Dog Dash tick.

THE EXPERIENCE

Suspension of disbelief about your natural size

THE TRICK

Creating larger-than-life ornaments that sell the premise

When you visit Toy Story Land, the theming suggests that you've shrunk down to the size of a toy. You're visiting Andy's backyard shown in the *Toy Story* movies, and he hasn't given any of his belongings to Bonnie yet. Yes, the gang's all here!

As the signature attraction at Toy Story Land, Slinky Dog Dash embodies the concept of the entire themed land. Everything that you see is part of a playset that Andy won during a fateful game at Toy Story Planet. He is now the proud owner of the Dash & Dodge Mega Coaster Kit, which he is happily constructing.

The catch is that Andy is a young boy, and I speak from experience when I say that young boys have the world's shortest attention spans. Presumably, Andy's seen something shiny or maybe chased a butterfly or something. Whatever happened, he hasn't completed the coaster kit yet, and that's troubling since you're about to ride it!

Yes, on Slinky Dog Dash, you're a kind of crash test dummy, the ill-fated toy forced to zoom around on an incomplete roller coaster. There's a strong chance that this won't end well for you, which exacerbates the element of excitement.

Imagineers really played up the premise with the ride design. You'll see all sorts of elements that reflect the improvisational skills of a child. Sure, it's a roller coaster playset, but it's got Christmas lights for some reason. Also, several of the beloved Toy Story characters are on display, probably because they're toys sharing the same play area with you.

From the start of the ride queue, you'll see hints of Andy's hand in building the playset. His illustrations are on display. You can see giant-sized characters like Jessie throughout the ride.

Disney's crafted a level of immersion that's stunning even by their lofty standards. By the time you board the ride, you'll fully believe that you're a toy in Andy's collection. And all Disney needed to perfect the illusion was a bunch of oversized models of Rex and Jenga blocks and the like. This easy demonstration of scale proves that the simplest tricks are frequently the most impacting.

THE EXPERIENCE

Mimicking the concept of a Slinky on a roller coaster

THE TRICK

Building a giant spring, a spring, a marvelous thing!

Sure, Epcot may have the reputation as Disney's park for infotainment, but the most scientific ride at Walt Disney World is Slinky Dog Dash. It's a brilliant demonstration of high-level physics concepts like kinetic energy, gravity, and the impact of momentum. In this way, it mirrors the Slinky itself.

Here's a quick history lesson for you. A retired naval engineer, Richard James, noticed a problem while he worked at the Philadelphia Naval Shipyard toward the end of World War II. Sailors passed along stories of their instruments struggling in the face of stormy weather. James deduced that the addition of a spring to these instruments would keep them stable in such scenarios.

The inventor imagined many practical military applications wherein the springs would prevent objects from falling at unwelcome moments. The Navy was nonplussed. They quickly passed on the idea. Thankfully, James' wife, Betty, envisioned a different usage. She thought these small springs could become educational but entertaining toys. She coined the name, Slinky, and the two of them sold the famous department store, Gimbels, on the idea. The rest is toy history.

When Imagineers learned that they would build a roller coaster based on the concept, they delighted in the possibilities. They wanted to display the scientific aspects of the Slinky during the brief roller coaster ride. Even though Slinky Dog Dash is only two minutes long, it does a remarkable job of highlighting the main scientific applications of the Slinky.

Some of the physics principles at play are the Law of Conservation, potential and kinetic energy, gravity, and Newton's First Law of Motion. Don't worry. This isn't an exam, and you won't be tested later. All you need to understand is the basic stuff to appreciate Slinky Dog Dash.

An object motion stays in motion. That's the Newtonian aspect. The Law of Conservation states that energy can't be created, but it also can't be destroyed. That's where potential and kinetic energy come into play. Something possesses energy whether it's stationary or in motion. The only question is whether it's static, which is potential energy, or kinetic energy.

With a Slinky, the object in question has a set amount of potential energy right up until you push it down the stairs Mexican Telenova style. Then, its energy transfers into the kinetic type. That object stays in motion thanks to another law of physics, gravity. That's what pulls it down the stairs. And that's how a Slinky works.

Imagineers wanted to re-create the concept of the Slinky with their roller coaster, and they did it by building a ride cart that mimics the design of the Slinky Dog from *Toy Story*. They made coaster carts that bend and turn individually. This design simulates the Slinky motion while demonstrating the Law of Conservation. It has that energy, whether it's moving or not, but the Slinky design is the demonstration of what this science looks like during a real-world application.

THE EXPERIENCE

A pregnant pause that ramps up the enthusiasm

THE TRICK

Bringing a full motion coaster to a full-stop

Slinky Dog Dash's coaster cart has potential energy that becomes kinetic once it gets revved up. But the genius part is neither the look nor the style of the roller coaster. It's the trick that occurs in the middle.

Disney stops the ride for a few seconds, ostensibly to enhance excitement for the concluding track elements. In actuality, it's another smart display of potential and kinetic energy. The object in motion feels the push of gravity against it and comes to a full stop. Then, after a delicious pause, it explodes into action once again.

The mechanics aren't complicated: just a simple braking system, the standard coaster acceleration mechanisms, and a countdown clock to heighten anticipation. It's the execution as well as the thought behind it that elevates the experience.

For starters, Disney had never constructed a roller coaster with a full stop in the middle before. Those are actually quite rare in the theme park industry. The engineering isn't hard, of course. You just re-locate the hardware customarily found at the start of the ride to the spot where you want to stop the coaster. Obviously, you need to install some brakes, too. This leads to the unique construction aspect that Slinky Dog Dash has elements from the start and end of a typical roller coaster squarely in its middle section. Weird, huh?

The thought behind this oddity is twofold. On the one hand, it ably demonstrates the high-level physics concepts on display with a Slinky. It celebrates the brilliance of one of the most popular toys of the 20th century. On the other hand, it's just plain fun, which is the whole point of a Disney ride, right? Slinky Dog Dash is highbrow under the hood, but it's something that a five-year-old will adore, too. Disney Imagineers snuck a massive amount of edutainment into a child-friendly roller coaster ride.

ABOUT THE AUTHOR

David is the co-founder of popular pop culture websites BoxOfficeProphets.com and HowWellDoYouKnow.com. David is blessed to work with some of the finest minds in the world through these two sites. He calls these friends, the site contributors, his Many Loves. To an individual, they're not just brilliant but also at the top of Maslow's Hierarchy. They are winning at life. David's only half a human without the love and support of all these incredible individuals.

David first visited Walt Disney World back when Future World was new, and his love of the original vision for the Experimental Prototype Community of Tomorrow remains to this day. His favorite ride is Spaceship Earth, a marvelous combination of architectural triumph and historical recreation of the dawn of man through modern times.

Today, David uses virtually all of his vacation days in Orlando, Florida, where he spends his disposable income buying new Stitch merchandise for his wife. When he's in Orlando, you'll find him meticulously checking his Fitbit to figure out how many miles he's walked that day at the parks. His current record is 14.6 miles. Obviously, he's a Park Hopper...with sore feet.

The content in this book was collated from David's writings at Theme Park Tourist. The very concept of Behind the Ride comes from the site's founder, the late Nick Sim, a wonderful person and gifted writer. David also thanks Amanda Leanne for her editing insights and feedback over the years. And Kim Hollis deserves a great deal of credit for being not just a spectacular person but also a patient editor, sounding board, and an all-around perfect wife.

The author also wants to thank his mother who—and this is not a joke—reads all his work so that she can correct any mistakes in her son's writing. His mother's passion for excellence is the reason why he's such a perfectionist in life.

This book is a loving tribute to the author's father, who died after a 14-year battle with cancer in 2014. A lifelong employee of the Eastman/Kodak Company, Howell Everette Mumpower always admired the infrastructure that supported industry, and that's why he lovingly introduced his children to EPCOT Center soon after its debut.

Had he chosen a different career path after he left the Navy, H.E. unquestionably would have become one of the finest writers in the world. These books are a son's way of carrying on the legacy of the far-better man who raised him.

ABOUT THEME PARK PRESS

Theme Park Press publishes books primarily about the Disney company, its history, culture, films, animation, and theme parks, as well as theme parks in general.

Our authors include noted historians, animators, Imagineers, and experts in the theme park industry.

We also publish many books by first-time authors, with topics ranging from fiction to theme park guides.

And we're always looking for new talent. If you'd like to write for us, or if you're interested in the many other titles in our catalog, please visit:

www.ThemeParkPress.com

Theme Park Press Newsletter

Subscribe to our free email newsletter and enjoy:

- Free book downloads and giveaways
- Access to excerpts from our many books
- Announcements of forthcoming releases
- Exclusive additional content and chapters
- And more good stuff available nowhere else

To subscribe, visit www.ThemeParkPress.com, or send email to newsletter@themeparkpress.com.

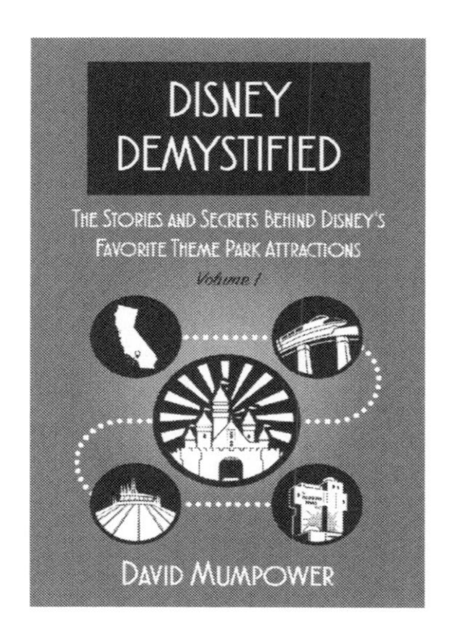
DISNEY
DEMYSTIFIED
THE STORIES AND SECRETS BEHIND DISNEY'S
FAVORITE THEME PARK ATTRACTIONS
Volume I
DAVID MUMPOWER

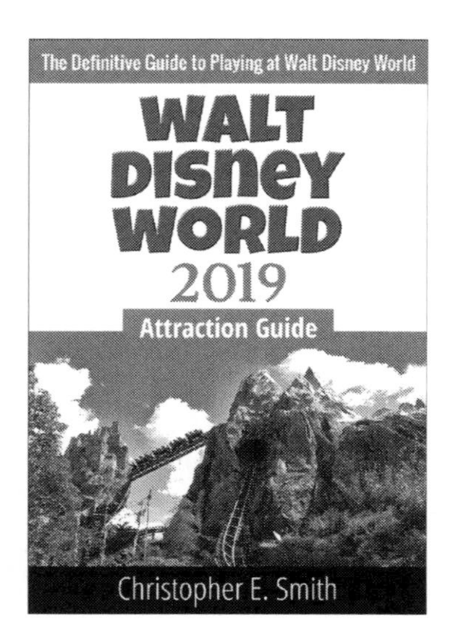
The Definitive Guide to Playing at Walt Disney World
WALT
DISNEY
WORLD
2019
Attraction Guide
Christopher E. Smith

INVENTING
DISNEYLAND
Alastair Dallas
The unauthorized story of the team that
made Walt Disney's dream come true

MORE
Secret
Stories of
Disneyland
Jim Korkis
DISNEYLAND

Printed in Poland
by Amazon Fulfillment
Poland Sp. z o.o., Wrocław

51648609R00103